Experiments in General Chemistry

Chem 1212L/1312L

Written and Compiled by Dr. Daphne Norton

macmillan learning
curriculum solutions

ISBN 978-1-5339-3484-0

Macmillan Learning Curriculum Solutions
14903 Pilot Drive
Plymouth, MI 48170
www.macmillanlearning.com

NortonD 3484-0 W21

Sustainability

Hayden-McNeil/Macmillan Learning Curriculum Solutions is proud to be a part of the larger sustainability initiative of Macmillan, our parent company. Macmillan has a goal to reduce its carbon emissions by 65% by 2020 from our 2010 baseline. Additionally, paper purchased must adhere to the Macmillan USA Paper Sourcing and Use Policy.

Hayden-McNeil partners with printers that use paper that is consistent with the environmental goals and values of Macmillan USA. This includes using paper certified by the Forest Stewardship Council (FSC), Sustainable Forestry Initiative (SFI), and/or the Programme for the Endorsement of Forest Certification (PEFC). We also offer paper with varying percentages of post-consumer waste as well as a 100% recycled stock. Additionally, Hayden-McNeil Custom Digital provides authors with the opportunity to convert print products to a digital format to use no paper at all. Visit http://sustainability.macmillan.com to learn more.

Table of Contents

General Information

Laboratory Experiments

Online Experiments & Exercises

Chem1212L/1312L
Laboratory Syllabus & Policies

Objective: The main objective of this course is to acquaint you with the techniques and equipment required to carry out basic chemistry experiments. The laboratory experiments are designed to demonstrate and test some of the basic principles taught in the lecture course. Your laboratory experience should be an interesting and rewarding opportunity to explore the topics covered in your lecture course.

In addition to basic laboratory techniques, you should gain the following skills:

- ability to analyze and evaluate raw data

- ability to record appropriately detailed procedures and accurate observations

- ability to understand your data and report data effectively with scientific integrity

- ability to relate laboratory work to the bigger picture and to recognize the applicability of scientific principles to real-world situations

- ability to apply critical thinking in the laboratory to recognize whether results and conclusions "make sense"

- ability to work effectively as part of a team

Attendance: Attendance will be taken at every laboratory session. Permission to attend a make-up lab section will be granted for emergencies and special circumstances. Appropriate documentation is required. Instructions for submitted a make-up request are posted under Content on eLC.

Students who arrive late to lab or who are dressed inappropriately will not be allowed to stay for the experiment and will not be given the opportunity to make-up the work.

Teaching Assistants: Your lab class will be taught by graduate teaching assistants. Your graduate TA will present a pre-lab lecture every week. You must arrive on time to hear the pre-lab lecture and special instructions for safety precautions and directions for waste disposal. Your graduate TA will grade your weekly assignments.

Academic Integrity

"I will be academically honest in all of my academic work and will not tolerate academic dishonesty of others." All students agree to abide by this code by signing the UGA Admissions Application.

"Academic Honesty" means performing all academic work without plagiarism, cheating, lying, tampering, stealing, giving or receiving unauthorized assistance from any other person, or using any source of information that is not common knowledge without properly acknowledging the source.

Violations of the academic honesty policy will be reported to the Office of Academic Honesty.

Handling Data

We expect you and your lab partner to have the same data. However, your answers to post-lab questions should be presented in your own words. You may not "borrow" data from another group. You need to analyze the data you collected in lab this semester. Data may not be modified or "fudged" to achieve desired results. If you realize there is a problem with your data, contact your TA for further instructions.

Submitting data you collected a previous semester or data collected by other students is a violation of the academic honesty policy. Information related to graded assignments should not be shared electronically or posted to websites or apps.

All of your assignments and experiments must be your original work. Cheating includes copying or using any data from another person, falsifying data by alteration or invention, or in any way submitting work or data not actually as you measured it while performing the experiment in our laboratory during this semester. Violations of the Academic Honesty Policy will be reported to the Office of the Vice President of Instruction.

Laboratory Materials/Equipment

Lab manual: You will record data and observations in the notebook portion of the lab manual and complete the report sheet for each experiment. The Report Sheet will be torn out of the lab manual and submitted to your TA.

Lab notebook: Record keeping is essential. You will use the notebook attached to this lab manual for recording data and observations. Details for Keeping a Lab Notebook are found on pages 16-17.

eLC: Weekly announcements will posted on the course site. Instructions for requesting make-up labs is also available on eLC. You are responsible for all course announcements posted to eLC.

- Grades will be posted on eLC and should be checked regularly. Questions about graded assignments should first be discussed with your TA and then with the Lab Director.

Safety Glasses & Goggles: Goggles or safety glasses with side shields are required for this course. You **must** wear safety glasses at all times during an experiment. Even if you wear eye glasses, you must wear additional eye protection. You should avoid wearing contacts in the lab.

Appropriate Lab Attire: You are required to wear closed-toe shoes and long pants when attending lab. You are also required to wear a cloth face mask. Details are outlined in the Safety Section on page 12.

Equipment: You are responsible for the maintenance of equipment and your station. You must return all borrowed materials to the appropriate place and leave the lab clean of chemicals, spills, and paper waste.

Broken glassware: You must dispose of all broken glassware in the appropriate box marked for broken glassware. If possible, rinse any chemical residue from the glassware before adding it to the box. Also, obtain a broken glassware slip and return it to the prep room to replace the broken glassware.

Attendance & Make-up Lab Policies

Students who miss a lab as a result of illness, accident, family emergency or a religious holiday will have the opportunity to make-up the experiment. Students attending university sponsored varsity athletic events may also make-up missed work.

Students wishing to attend make-up lab must complete an online survey hosted on Qualtrics.

- Appropriate documentation is required in order to process a make-up request. Make-up requests will not be approved without documentation. Hand written notes on a sheet of paper will not be approved. The Student Health Center will provide a note upon request.
- Make-up labs will be conducted via Zoom.
- The make-up labs will follow the same schedule as the regular labs. They will be conducted the Friday afternoon following the scheduled experiment. Make-up labs will not be conducted anytime else during the semester.

Excused Absences

If a student has a prolonged illness or other reason that prevents attendance at make-up lab, the student will be excused from the assignment. A request for an excused absence must be submitted within 10 business days of the absence. (A submission with supporting documentation is required.)

- Students who arrive late to lab or who are dressed inappropriately will not be allowed to stay for the experiment and will not be given the opportunity to make-up the work or attend make-up lab.
- Providing false statements regarding an absence is also a violation of the Academic Honesty Policy.

Students who miss more than three experiments (regardless of the reason) will receive an Incomplete in the course and will need to complete the work the following semester.

Assignments

Preparation

You should read and study each experiment before coming to lab and record the purpose and procedure in your lab notebook. Your TA will check your lab notebook as you enter the classroom. If your notebook is not complete, you will not be allowed to attend the lab. *See pages 17-18 in the lab manual for directions on keeping a lab notebook.*

At the end of each lab period, your TA will check your notebook and sign you out of lab.

Report Sheets

Each week you will submit the report sheet for the experiment you performed. The report sheet will be due at the end of the lab period. You should check eLC every week for details of your assignment.

Quizzes

Quizzes will cover the experiments performed this semester. Questions may cover procedural details, calculations, data analysis and background information related to the experiments. Most quizzes will be administered through eLC. To avoid technical problems, students should not use a wifi connection when taking the quiz.   Students are encouraged to take the quizzes in a computer center in the Science Library or the Miller Learning Center.

Withdrawal

Students who withdraw from lecture must also withdraw from the laboratory course. The courses are co-requisites.

Chemistry Laboratory Safety

- Absolutely no food, drink, gum, or tobacco products should be consumed in the laboratory. Water bottles should be stored in backpacks.

- You must wear eye protection at all times while in the laboratory! Goggles or safety glass must be worn over regular eye glasses.

©Hayden-McNeil, LLC

- <u>You must wear pants to lab</u>. Shorts, leggings, and short skirts are not appropriate. You may not wear jeans with large rips or tears.

- Sandals may not be worn in lab. You should wear closed-toe shoes.

- The lab is equipped with a safety shower and eyewash.

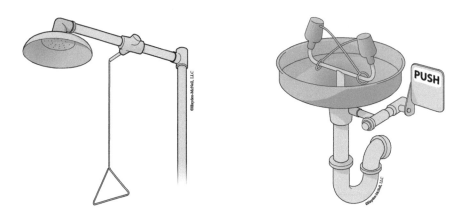

- All chemical waste must be placed in the appropriate waste bin located in the fume hood. Always check with your TA before pouring any chemicals down the drain.

Chemical Safety

- Caution should be used when handling chemicals.

- Safety Data Sheets are available for each chemical in the lab.

- If you spill any acid, base or other chemical, contact your TA immediately.

- Thoroughly wash your skin of any chemical contaminants.

- If any chemical gets in your eye, you must contact the TA immediately and proceed to the eyewash station. It may be helpful to have another student assist you in walking to the eyewash or alerting your TA.

- If you encounter a chemical splash or a fire, you must immediately go to the safety shower. Alert the TA who will assist you during the emergency.

- Dispose of chemical waste in the appropriate waste container located in the hood. Carefully read the label and do not mix waste materials as this may result in a dangerous chemical reaction. DO NOT pour any chemicals down the drain without permission from your TA.

General Equipment Usage

(1) In the event of glassware breakage, contact your TA who will assist you in cleaning up the accident. All broken glassware should be placed in the broken glassware receptacle.

(2) Keep the work area free of debris. No trash or chemicals should be left on the bench tops.

(3) Any equipment taken from the drawers or shelves should be returned to its appropriate place.

(4) Hotplates should be close to room temperature before returning to the shelf.

(5) Cords should be wrapped around the hotplates and stir plates before returning the item to the shelf.

(6) Check that the gas outlets and water faucets have been turned off after use.

(7) You must clean any spills and trash before leaving the lab. Your TA should check your work station before signing you out.

Beaker

A general purpose container for holding or mixing liquids with a pouring spout. Some beakers have graduations indicating approximate volume of contents.

Erlenmeyer flask

A general purpose container used for holding or mixing liquids. Some flasks have graduations on them to indicate approximate volume of contents.

Filtering flask

A heavy wall flask designed for use in suction (vacuum) filtration of solutions. Has side hose connection to attach vacuum tubing.

Volumetric flask

A flask used for preparation of solutions. Volumetric flasks are calibrated to contain a specific volume of liquid or solution.

Test tube

A round-bottom glass tube used to contain or heat small amounts of materials.

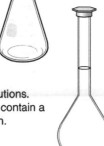

Volumetric pipet

A pipet calibrated to deliver an exact amount of solvent or solution.

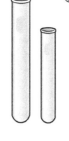

Mohr pipet

A graduated pipet used to deliver a solvent or solution.

Buret

A buret is calibrated to dispense liquid through a stopcock.

Funnel

Funnels are used for adding liquid to narrow mouth containers, or, with filter paper, for filtering solutions.

Powder funnel

A funnel with a short, wide stem for use in pouring powders into narrow mouth containers.

Buchner funnel

A porous funnel used with filter paper during vacuum filtration.

Rubber policeman

A rubber tip with a flattened end used on a glass rod for scraping solids from containers.

Spatula and scoopula

For handling small amounts of solid chemicals.

Graduated cylinder

A measuring device, graduated to contain liquids or solutions. Tall cylinders should be equipped with a plastic bumper to absorb impact if the cylinder is tipped over.

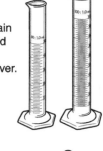

Dropping pipet

A medicine dropper used to deliver liquids in dropwise amounts.

Pasteur pipet

A capillary tip dropper used to deliver small drops. These are usually disposable.

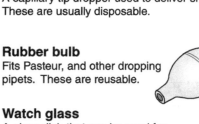

Rubber bulb

Fits Pasteur, and other dropping pipets. These are reusable.

Watch glass

A glass dish that can be used for evaporation of small amounts of liquids, for studying small amounts of solids, or as covers for beakers.

Bunsen burner

A burner that contains a needle valve for gas flow regulation.

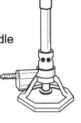

Ring stand support

Consists of a heavy base with a metal rod for supporting apparatus for a variety of laboratory operations.

Utility clamp

Adjustable clamp for holding a test tube, flask, buret, or other apparatus.

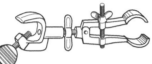

Extension clamp

Used with a clamp holder, allows more variation in positioning than a utility clamp.

3-prong clamp

Used with a clamp holder, allows for more versatility in holding different types of apparatus.

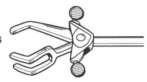

Extension clamp holder

Used to attach an extension clamp to a ring stand support or support frame.

Support ring

Designed as a base support for beakers or flasks when heated on a ring stand support.

Double buret holder

A double clamp for holding two burets.

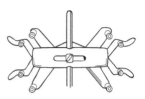

Wire gauze (ceramic center)

A support surface to be used with a ring support or tripod to provide uniform heat distribution to a flask or beaker.

Stir bar

A teflon coated magnet used for mixing reactions.

Magnetic stirrer

A device used to stir reaction mixtures.

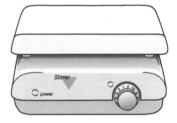

pH and mV meter / thermometer

A device used to measure pH, mV, and temperature.

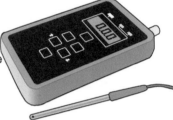

Test tube holder

A clamp secures the test tube in place.

Beaker tongs

Wide-jaw tongs for holding beakers.

Crucible tongs

Tongs with oval opening in jaws for holding crucibles. Tips used for handling crucible covers.

©Hayden-McNeil, LLC

Chemistry 1212/1312 Equipment & Lab Policies

Name (print): _____   Group: _____

Day and time of Lab Section: _____   TA: _____

(1) I am aware of the safety precautions that must be taken when handling chemicals. I agree to wear safety glasses or goggles at all times when in the lab room. I will also wear a lab coat, closed-toed shoes and a mask.

(2) I know the location of the safety shower, fire extinguisher and eyewash. I will notify my TA if there is a spill.

(3) I am responsible for the care of the glassware and equipment at my work station and the assigned analytical balance. Any broken glassware should be replaced at the time of the breakage.

(4) I understand that I am responsible for maintaining a clean safe work space. I know the glassware must be cleaned and dried at the end of the lab period. I will also wipe down my work space and discard any trash.

(5) I realize that an important part of doing science is producing valid, reproducible data. I also realize cheating and falsification of data including using data from another student or a previous semester is a violation of the Honor Code.

(6) I am familiar with the lab make-up policies and understand the requirements for attending a virtual make-up lab. I know that make-up requests are submitted online via Qualtrics.

_____
Student Signature/Date

_____
TA Signature/Date

Instructions for Keeping a Laboratory Notebook

- You will be required to keep a lab notebook. The notebook is attached to the lab manual. To prepare for each laboratory experiment, you must read the assigned experiment in the manual or the provided handout.

- **Prior to arrival in lab**, you should read the lab and record the purpose and procedure in your notebook. The purpose and procedure should be in your own words and not merely copied from the manual. You should include enough detail that you could complete the experiment with your notebook alone, without the aid of your lab manual.

Rules for keeping a notebook:

- All observations, calculations and data should be recorded into your bound notebook using blue or black ink. No pencil!

- Write directly into your notebook during data collection. Do not record data in your manual to be transferred to the notebook later.

- No white out! All markings are permanent. If you need to correct a mistake, simply draw a single line through the word or phrase in error.

- No pages may be torn or removed from the lab notebook.

- Each section must be clearly labeled. Leave appropriate space between sections to make notes and observations. Your laboratory instructor must sign your notebook before you leave each session.

- There may also be spot checks any time during the semester.

Your notebook should not be modified after you have recorded data and observations. Any additional information that is added should include your initials and the date that it is added. You should not write study notes in your lab notebook. It is a site for recording data and observations.

Notebook Format

Page One   Title page includes course title, section number, semester, date and your name.

Page Two   Table of Contents should include each experiment and its beginning page number.

Overall format for writing up each experiment

1) *Experiment title and date performed. Partner's name if lab was a team effort.*

2) *Purpose*: two or three sentences of your own words to explain what you are attempting to determine and the method used.

3) *Procedure*: a concise step by step outline of exactly what you must do to perform the experiment

4) *Data/Observations*: all measurements you make (time, length, volume) and descriptions of what you see (color changes, precipitation)

5) *Calculations*: show ALL calculations required to answer questions and problems for report sheets. Whenever applicable an experimental value should be compared to a known or theoretical value. The source of the known value should be cited. Percent error should be calculated to compare known and experimental values.

6) *Conclusions*: a brief statement in your own words to summarize the experiment. If the results were unexpected, cite possible sources of error. The conclusion should be scientific and practical, not a personal reaction to the lab. Opinions and personal statements are not valid, such as "the lab was fun." Also, a statement such as "this experiment was successful" is not sufficient without explanation.

Graphing with Excel 2010

Data analysis is an essential part of chemistry. In order to evaluate data, scientists often utilize a spreadsheet program such as Excel. A common application is graphing data.

Data Input

Open a new spreadsheet and enter the data you intend to graph:

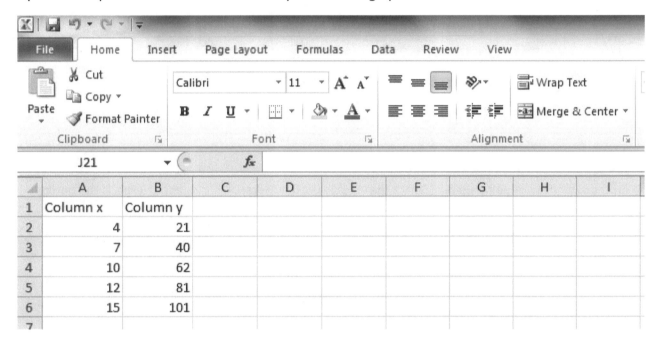

Creating a Graph

Highlight the data columns to graph. Select the "Insert" tab and click on the "Scatter" button.

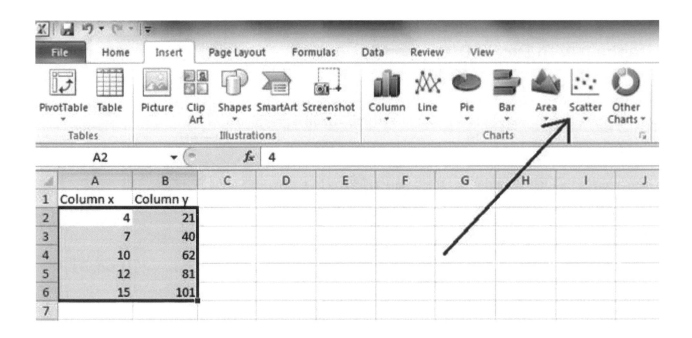

A drop down menu should appear. Select the "Scatter with Markers Only" button. (This is the button that only shows points; no lines.)

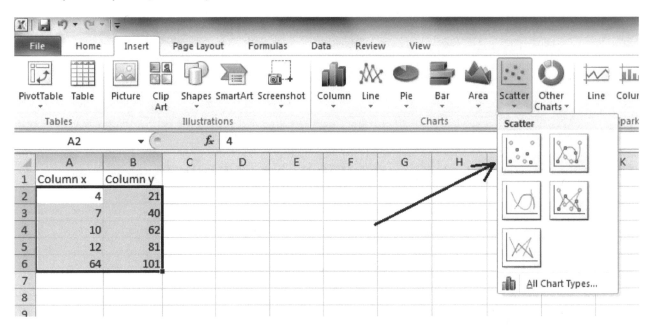

You should now have a graph displaying your data points.

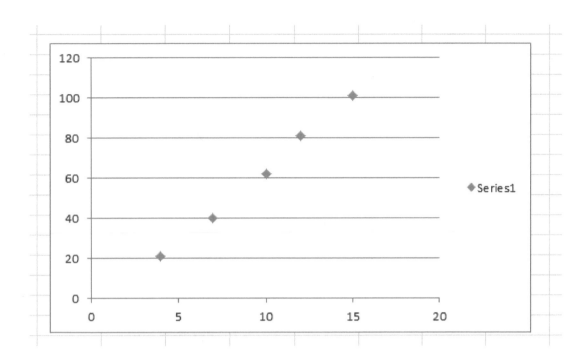

Adding Titles

First, click on the chart (graph.) Next, click on the "Layout" tab.

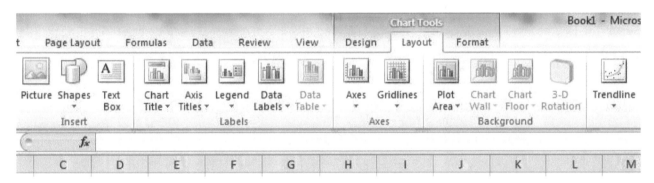

Click on the "Chart Title" button to add a title and use the "Axis Titles" button to label your axes.

Adding a Trendline

First, click on the chart (graph.) While in the Layout menu, select the "Trendline" button. Go to More Trendline options.

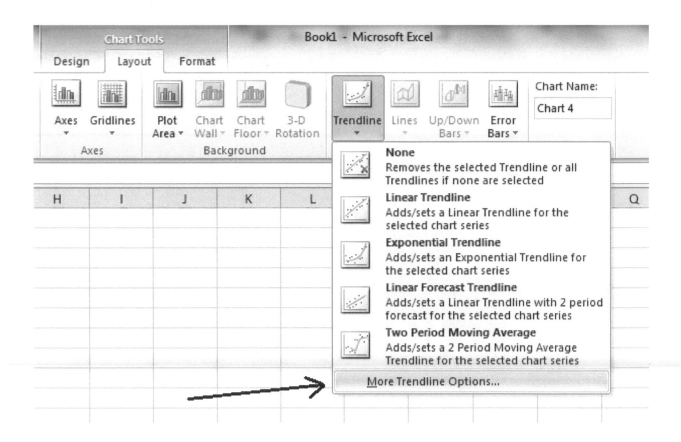

Select the Regression Type. Most of the data analyzed in general chemistry will be linear.

Select the boxes that say "Display Equation on Chart" and "Display R-squared value on chart." The R-squared value is a statistical measure of how close the data are to the fitted regression line. The closer to 1.0, the better the fit.

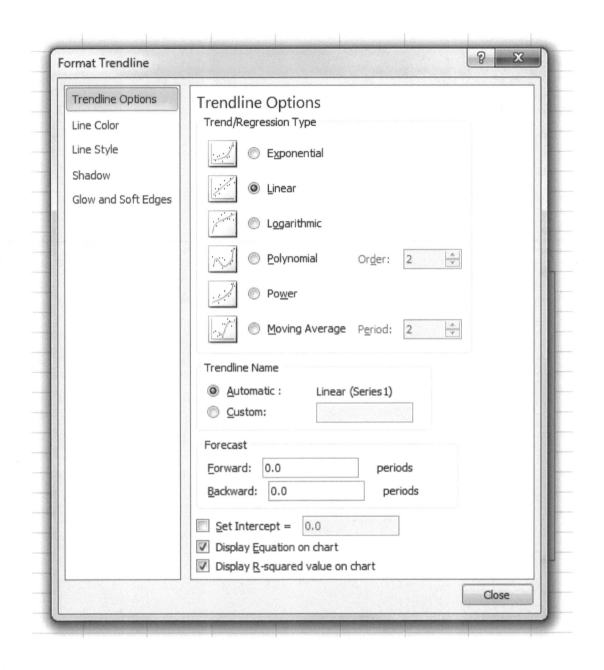

Your final graph should include a title, a label for each axis and the appropriate units. Display the equation of the line and the R-squared value. When analyzing an unknown sample, you may create a calibration plot. In this case, if your R-squared value is too far away from 1.0, you should repeat your experiment before analyzing any unknown samples.

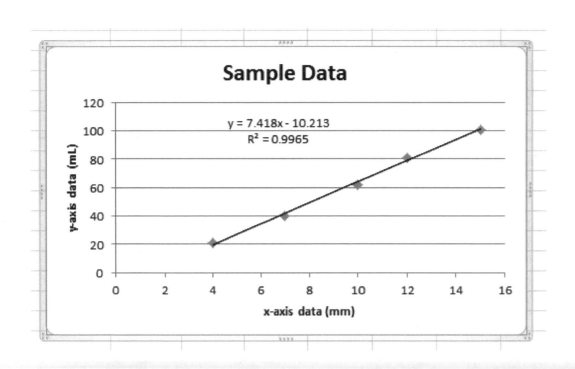

Laboratory Experiments

Chem 1212L/1312L /1412L

Experiment 1
Freezing Point Depression Or A Lesson in Making Ice Cream

"I scream! You scream! We all scream for ice cream!" People rarely get excited about colligative properties, but they should. Colligative properties help us make ice cream! Freezing point depression is a colligative property.

Let us consider how freezing point depression aids in the preparation of ice cream. You can quickly freeze your own ice cream with some salt and ice. Place the ingredients (milk, sugar, cream) in a quart size re-sealable plastic bag.[1] Seal the bag. Fill a larger bag (gallon size) with 2 cups of ice and ½ cup of sodium chloride (table salt.) Place the sealed bag of ingredients inside the larger bag with ice and salt. Seal the larger bag. Gently rock the bag back and forth. You may want to wear gloves or place a towel around the bag. Continue to rock the bag for 10-15 minutes. Voila! You now have ice cream.

outdoorsman/Shutterstock.com

What is happening on the molecular level? You are freezing the liquid ice cream ingredients. Heat is transferred from the ice cream mixture to the ice and rock salt. Ice cream freezes at a temperature lower than the freezing point of water. This is why rock salt is added to the ice. You cannot use plain ice to chill the ice cream. The ice will melt before the base gets cold enough. By adding salt to the ice, you lower the freezing point of the ice. The ice/salt mixture reaches a temperature lower enough to freeze the ice cream base. [2]

In this experiment, we will determine the molar mass of isopropyl alcohol by investigating the freezing point depression observed in an aqueous solution containing the alcohol. *Colligative properties* depend only on the number and not on the identity of the solute particles in a solution. We discussed freezing point depression. Other colligative properties include osmotic pressure and boiling point elevation.

Freezing point is the temperature at which the solvent in solution and the pure solid solvent have the same vapor pressure. Basically, the solid and liquid are coexisting. When a solute is added, the vapor pressure of the solvent changes and causes the vapor pressure of the liquid solvent to be lowered. The solute particles are interfering or standing between the solvent particles. This causes intermolecular forces to be weakened. Therefore, lower temperatures are required to make it possible for the solvent particles to reach each other and form the solid.

The freezing point of a solvent is lowered when any solute is dissolved in that solvent. The nature of the solute is not important, only the amount of the solute. We can quantify the freezing point depression because it is proportional to the amount of solute present in a given mass of solvent. The molality of the solute is needed to calculate the freezing point depression. *Molality* (m) is defined as the moles of solute per kilogram of solvent. In our case, it will be the moles of isopropyl alcohol divided by the mass of water in kg.

$$m = moles\ solute/kg\ solvent$$

The freezing point depression Δt_f is a measure of the difference between the freezing point of the solution and the freezing point of the pure solvent. In our case, the pure solvent is water.

$$\Delta t_f = t_{f\ solution} - t_{f\ solvent}$$

The freezing point depression is related to molality and the freezing point depression constant, K_f. The value of K_f is characteristic for a solvent. The K_f

value for water is -1.86 °C/m. The van't Hoff factor, i, considers the number of dissolved particles the solute contributes.

$$\Delta t_f = i\, K_f\, m$$

You can experimentally determine the molar mass of a solute by measuring the freezing point depression and rearranging the equation.

$$m = \Delta t_f / i\, K_f$$

$$m \text{ (kg solvent)} = \text{moles solute}$$

$$(\text{mass solute})/(\text{moles solute}) = \text{molar mass of solute}$$

Procedure

Set up a freezing point apparatus as demonstrated by your instructor. The apparatus consists of a large test tube, a two-hole stopper with wire stirrer and digital thermometer as seen in Figure 1.1. *Be careful not to push the stopper too far into the test tube.*

Prepare a water/ice/rock salt bath by adding equal amounts of ice and rock salt and a small amount of water in the 600 mL beaker. Stir the mixture and check the temperature of the bath. It should be at -10 °C.   If the bath is too warm, you may need to decant some water or add more ice/rock salt.

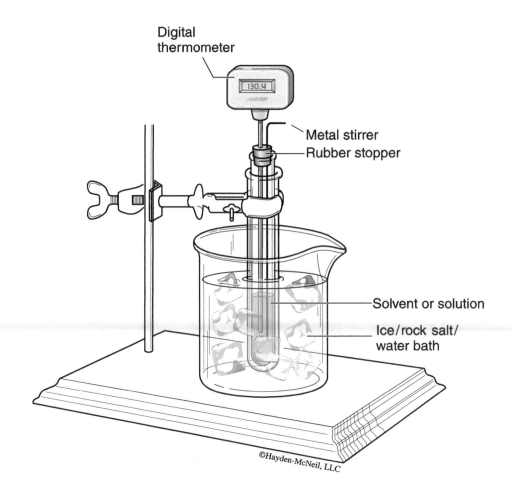

Figure 1.1 The wire stirrer will be used to determine if the solution has frozen.

Measure 25.0 mL of distilled water with a graduated cylinder. Transfer the water to the test tube of the freezing point depression apparatus.

Use the stirrer to agitate the water in the test tube. Record the time and temperature at 30-second intervals. Continue recording the temperature until the temperature value has been constant for five consecutive readings. (If the water has frozen sufficiently to impair stirring, record the temperature.) Allow the frozen water to thaw and repeat the procedure.

Allow the frozen water to thaw and prepare for the next experiment. Add 6-7 mL of isopropyl alcohol into the test tube. Use a buret to dispense an exact volume of alcohol. Record the volume to the hundredths place. Stopper the test tube and place it in the bath. Again, stir the solution and record the temperature at 30-second intervals. Continue until the readings are the same for five consecutive measurements or the solution has become difficult to stir. Allow the frozen mixture to thaw and repeat the procedure.

References

(1) Ice cream recipe: ½ cup milk, ½ cup whipping cream (heavy cream), ¼ cup sugar, ¼ teaspoon vanilla

(2) http://www.rsc.org/education/eic/issues/2003July/Makingicecream.asp

Name: _____

Instructor: _____

Experimental Data

Density of isopropyl alcohol   0.785 g/mL

	Trial 1	**Trial 2**
Final buret reading	_____	_____
Initial buret reading	_____	_____
Volume of isopropyl alcohol	_____	_____
Mass of isopropyl alcohol used	_____	_____
t_f, water	_____	_____
t_f, mixture	_____	_____
Δt_f	_____	_____
molality (experimental)	_____	_____
moles isopropyl alcohol in sample	_____	_____
molar mass of isopropyl alcohol	_____	_____

Show *molality* calculations for one trial. Include proper units and significant figures.

Show the calculations for the number of moles of isopropyl alcohol in the sample.

Percent Error. Calculate of the molar mass of isopropyl alcohol and report the percent error between the experimental value and the literature value.

Post-Lab Questions:

(1) Explain the difference between molarity and molality.

(2) The city manager is trying to decide what materials to order to prepare for the winter months ahead. She asks you if she should order sodium chloride, calcium chloride, or potassium chloride. The supplier can offer all three salts at a comparable price when ordering in bulk. What advice will you give her? Explain your reasoning.

(3) A 300.0 mg sample of caffeine was dissolved in 10.0 g of camphor (K_f = 39.7 °C/kgmol.) The freezing point of camphor decreases by 3.07 °C. What is the calculated molar mass of caffeine? Show your work.

(4) Compare the calculated molar mass of caffeine with the known molar mass of caffeine. Based on this information, what should be van't Hoff factor be for caffeine? Explain.

Experiment 2
Chemical Kinetics

Chemical kinetics is an area of chemistry that focuses on reaction rates. The reaction rate of a chemical reaction is defined as the change in concentration of a reactant or product per unit time. The molar concentration of a reactant will decrease over time and the molar concentration of product will increase.

There are many practical applications of kinetics. An important branch of science is pharmacokinetics. This field studies the process by which a drug is absorbed, distributed, metabolized and eliminated from the body. For example, the mechanisms for the sustained release of drugs are based on the half-life of the substances used and sometimes the pH of the body as well. Practically, this affects the way in which dosages are determined and prescribed.

Chemical kinetics is also used in environmental studies to model the rate of ozone depletion in the atmosphere and to study migration of pesticides in soil systems. It has many industrial applications as well. Engineers study the rate of corrosion on metal and the mechanical behavior of rubber. Many chemical companies have entire teams of scientists devoted to catalysis. **Catalysis** is the increase in rate of a chemical reaction due to the participation of a substance called a **catalyst**. A catalyst lowers the activation energy of a reaction. Upon addition of a catalyst, the reaction may proceed at a faster rate or under different conditions (as at a lower temperature) than otherwise possible. Unlike other reagents in the chemical reaction, a catalyst is not consumed. It is estimated that 90% of all commercially produced chemical products involve a catalyst at some stage in the process of their manufacture. [1]

The rate of a reaction is dependent on the concentration of reactants. (If a catalyst is involved it is also dependent on the catalyst.) Consider the example shown below.

$$2NO(g) + 2H_2(g) \rightarrow N_2(g) + 2H_2O(g)$$

The reaction rate was experimentally determined to be Rate = k $[NO]^2[H_2]$. The reaction is second order with respect to NO and first order with respect to H_2. If the concentration of hydrogen is doubled, the overall reaction rate will double. If the concentration of NO is doubled, the overall reaction rate will be quadrupled. The overall rate law is the sum of all exponents. In this case, it is third order.

It is very important to realize that the exponent representing the order of each reactant cannot be determined by the written equation. It must be determined experimentally.

Temperature Dependence of a Reaction Rate: Arrhenius Equation

The temperature dependence of reaction rate is expressed through the rate constant. For most reactions, the rate constant varies with temperature according to the Arrhenius Equation:

$$k = Ae^{-E_a/RT}$$

In this equation, e is the base of natural logarithms, R is the gas constant 8.314 J/(K mol), and T is absolute temperature. An increase in temperature will lead to a larger k value and consequently a higher reaction rate. A is the frequency factor, a constant that reflects the frequency of collisions with proper orientation. Finally, Ea is the activation energy for the reaction. The activation energy is the difference in energy between the reactants and the transition state as shown in Figure 2.1.

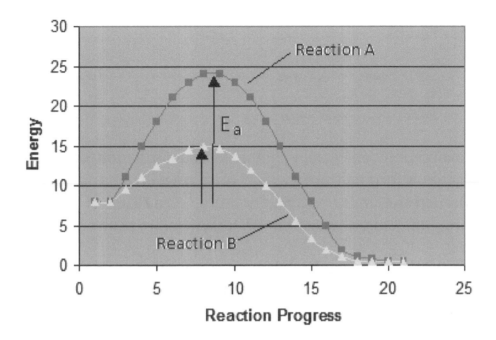

Figure 2.1   Reaction A will have a slower rate than Reaction B because it has a greater activation energy.

Determining a Rate Law [2]

In this experiment, we will determine the rate law and activation energy for the reaction of iron (III) ion with iodide ion to form iron (II) ion and triiodide ion.

$$2 Fe^{3+}(aq) + 3 I^-(aq) \longrightarrow 2 Fe^{2+}(aq) + I_3^-(aq)$$

The rate law can be written as Reaction Rate = $k[Fe^{3+}]^m[I^-]^n$.

Our task is to determine the value for the exponents m and n. This can only be done experimentally. The reaction rate can be written in terms of triiodide ion formation as follows.

$$Rate = \Delta[I_3^-]/\Delta t$$

Unfortunately, there is no practical way to measure the reaction rate directly. However, we can couple the iron (III) – iodide reaction with another reaction and monitor those results.

$$2\ Fe^{3+}(aq)\ +\ 3\ I^-(aq)\ \longrightarrow\ 2\ Fe^{2+}(aq)\ +\ I_3^-(aq)$$

$$I_3^-(aq)\ +\ 2\ S_2O_3^{2-}(aq)\ \longrightarrow\ 3\ I^-\ (aq)\ +\ S_4O_6^{2-}\ (aq)$$

During the experiment, $Fe^{3+}(aq)$ is combined with $I^-(aq)$ *and* $S_2O_3^{2-}(aq)$. The triiodide ion that is formed from the first reaction will react further with thiosulfate ion present in the reaction mixture. As a result of this coupling, the rate of the iron (III) – iodide reaction can be written in terms of thiosulfate ion as follows.

$$Rate = \Delta[I_3^-]/\Delta t = -1/2\ \{\Delta[S_2O_3^{2-}]/\Delta t\}$$

By following the change in concentration of thiosulfate ion, the rate of the iron (III) – iodide reaction may be determined.

We can use this coupling reaction because we have a way of monitoring the concentration of thiosulfate ion. Starch is also added to the reaction mixture. Any triiodide ion that does not react with thiosulfate ion will form a dark blue complex with starch.

$$I_3^-(aq)\ +\ starch(aq) \longrightarrow\ \ \ starch\text{-}I_3^-\ complex\ (blue)$$

Triiodide ion will react with $S_2O_3^{2-}$ (instead of starch) as long as $S_2O_3^{2-}$ is present. As long as thiosulfate ion remains, the solution will be colorless. When the thiosulfate ion has reacted completely, the remaining triiodide ion will be free to form the complex with starch. The solution will turn blue.

In each trial that is carried out during the experiment, the concentration of $S_2O_3^{2-}$ will be 0.00040 M. The time required for complete disappearance of $S_2O_3^{2-}$ is equal to the time required for the solution to turn blue. Consequently, the rate of the iron (III) – iodide reaction is given as

$$Rate = -1/2\ \{\Delta[S_2O_3^{2-}]/\Delta t\} = -1/2\ \{(0.00040\ M)/\Delta t\}$$

where Δt is the time required for the reaction to turn blue. This is the time interval from mixing reactants to formation of the blue complex.

Determination of the Reaction Order

To determine the exponents in the rate law (i.e. the reaction order), it is necessary to establish how the rate is related to the concentration of each reactant. This requires holding the concentration of one reactant constant while varying the concentration of the other reactant. Any observable change in reaction rate can then be attributed to one particular reactant.

Recall the form of the rate law for the iron (III) – iodide reaction.

$$\text{Rate} = k[Fe^{3+}]^m[I^-]^n$$

Taking the natural logarithm of both sides, the equation becomes as follows

$$\ln(\text{Rate}) = \ln(k) + \ln([Fe^{3+}]^m) + \ln([I^-]^n)$$

or

$$\ln(\text{Rate}) = \ln(k) + m \cdot \ln([Fe^{3+}]) + n \cdot \ln([I^-])$$

If $[I^-]$ is held constant while $[Fe^{3+}]$ is changed, then $n \cdot \ln([I^-])$ is a constant. Since k is also a constant, the two factors can be combined, and the equation becomes

$$\ln(\text{Rate}) = m \cdot \ln([Fe^{3+}]) + \ln(\text{constant})$$

This equation is written in the form of a straight line where $y = \ln(\text{Rate})$ and $x = \ln([Fe^{3+}])$. A plot of $\ln(\text{Rate})$ versus $\ln([Fe^{3+}])$ will give a straight line with slope equal to m, the order of the reaction with respect to Fe^{3+}.

If $[Fe^{3+}]$ is held constant while $[I^-]$ is changed, then $m \cdot \ln([Fe^{3+}])$ is a constant, and the equation becomes

$$\ln(\text{Rate}) = n \cdot \ln([I^-]) + \ln(\text{constant})$$

This equation is written in the form of a straight line where y = ln(Rate) and x = ln([I⁻]). A plot of ln(Rate) versus ln([I⁻]) will give a straight line with slope equal to n, the order of the reaction with respect to I⁻.

Procedure

Beaker A

Trial #	0.04M Fe^{3+} (mL)	0.15 M HNO_3 (mL)	H_2O (mL)
1	5.00	10.00	10.00
2	7.50	7.50	10.00
3	10.00	5.00	10.00
4	12.50	2.50	10.00
5	5.00	10.00	10.00
6	5.00	10.00	10.00
7	5.00	10.00	10.00

Beaker B

Trial #	0.04 M KI (mL)	0.004 M $S_2O_3^{2-}$ (mL)	Starch (mL)	H_2O (mL)
1	5.00	5.00	2.50	12.50
2	5.00	5.00	2.50	12.50
3	5.00	5.00	2.50	12.50
4	5.00	5.00	2.50	12.50
5	2.50	5.00	2.50	15.00
6	7.50	5.00	2.50	10.00
7	10.00	5.00	2.50	7.50

Prepare the two solutions for trial 1 shown in the table above. Use pipets to add the appropriate volume of reagents to beaker A and beaker B. The volumes must be exact. Record the temperature of the solutions to 0.1°C. Add the contents of beaker A to beaker B *and* start a stopwatch timer simultaneously. Swirl the solution to make certain the contents are well mixed. Stop the timer when the reaction mixture reaches a blue color. (The actual shade of blue when the reaction is stopped is subjective. Make certain that whatever the shade of blue used, each trial is taken to that same exact shade of blue. Be consistent.) Record the time. Dispose of the solution by diluting the mixture with water and pouring down the sink. Clean and dry the beakers. Repeat this process for trials 2 through 7.

Beaker A

Trial #	Temp	0.04M Fe^{3+} (mL)	0.15 M HNO_3 (mL)	H_2O (mL)
8	RT	5.00	10.00	10.00
9	high	5.00	10.00	10.00
10	low	5.00	10.00	10.00

Beaker B

Trial #	Temp	0.04 M KI (mL)	0.004 M $S_2O_3^{2-}$ (mL)	Starch (mL)	H_2O (mL)
8	RT	5.00	5.00	2.50	12.50
9	high	5.00	5.00	2.50	12.50
10	low	5.00	5.00	2.50	12.50

Next, you will study the reaction at varying temperatures. You have already collected data at room temperature. (This was done in trial 1. The data from trial 1 can be used for trial 8.) The reaction will also be carried out at a temperature approximately 5°C higher than room temperature. A water bath will be used to maintain the elevated temperature. Your instructor will provide instructions for using the water bath. Add reagents to beaker A and beaker B as indicated in the table. Place the two beakers into the water bath, and allow them to sit for a few minutes to reach temperature equilibrium. Be careful not to allow any mixing of the reaction solution with the water in the bath. The beakers must be monitored at all times. Once the solutions have reached the appropriate temperature, add the contents of beaker A to beaker B and start the timer. Record the temperature of the solution to 0.1°C. Swirl to mix the contents, and place the beaker back into the water bath. Stop the timer when the reaction mixture reaches a blue color. Record the time, and dispose of the solution.

The reaction must also be carried out at a temperature approximately 5°C lower than room temperature. Proceed as in trial #9 using a cold water bath.

Waste Disposal
Acidic solutions (0.15 M HNO_3 and 0.04 M $Fe(NO_3)_3$ in 0.15 M HNO_3) should be neutralized, then diluted and poured down the sink. All other solutions should be diluted and poured down the sink.

References

(1) "Recognizing the Best in Innovation: Breakthrough Catalyst". *R&D Magazine*, September 2005, p. 20.

(2) Burkart, Maureen. This experiment was developed in collaboration with faculty from Georgia Perimeter College.

Name: _____

Instructor: _____

Part I: Reaction Rate Data

Concentration of $S_2O_3^{2-}$ _____

Trial	Initial Temperature °C	Reaction Time (Δt, sec)
1	_____	_____
2	_____	_____
3	_____	_____
4	_____	_____
5	_____	_____
6	_____	_____
7	_____	_____
8	_____	_____
9	_____	_____
10	_____	_____

Trial	Initial Rate	ln Rate
1	_____	_____
2	_____	_____
3	_____	_____
4	_____	_____
5	_____	_____
6	_____	_____
7	_____	_____
8	_____	_____
9	_____	_____
10	_____	_____

Part II: Reaction Rate with respect to $[I^-]$ and $[Fe^{3+}]$

Trial	$[I^-]$	ln $[I^-]$	$[Fe^{3+}]$	ln $[Fe^{3+}]$
1				
2				
3				
4				
5				
6				
7				
8				
9				
10				

Prepare two graphs   The first graph will plot ln(Rate) versus ln[Fe^{3+}]. The second graph will plot ln(Rate) versus ln [I^-].   Attach the graphs to your report sheet.

Using the data from the graphs, write the rate law for the reaction:

Discuss sources of error for the kinetics experiment. What effect should these sources of error have on the experimental results?

Experiment 3

The Complex Ion Equilibrium of Fe (III) and Thiocyanate Ions

Many chemical reactions involve an equilibrium process. During a dynamic equilibrium, the rate of the forward reaction equals the rate of the reverse reaction.

Given an equilibrium reaction

$$aA + bB \rightleftharpoons cC + dD \tag{1}$$

The **Law of Mass Action** proposes that we can write the following equilibrium constant expression

$$K_{eq} = [C]^c [D]^d/[A]^a [B]^b \tag{2}$$

K_{eq} is called the equilibrium constant. The square brackets indicate concentrations in moles per liter, (mole/L), and the lower case a, b, c, and d represent the stoichiometric coefficients in the balanced equation.

This equation is not only applied to chemical reactions, physicists use this equation to study electron flow through semiconductors. The law of mass action also forms the basis of the compartmental model of disease spread in mathematical epidemiology. In addition, ecologists use this equation to model predator-prey relationships.

In today's experiment you will investigate the equilibrium of the following reaction:

$$Fe^{3+} + SCN^- \rightleftharpoons FeSCN^{2+} \qquad (3)$$

The equilibrium constant expression for this reaction is:

$$K_{eq} = [FeSCN^{2+}]/[Fe^{3+}][SCN^-] \qquad (4)$$

To prevent formation of complex ions other than that shown in equation 3, the concentration of ferric ions is kept large in relationship to the thiocyanate ions.

To determine the value of any equilibrium constant, a method of measuring concentrations must be found. The Fe^{3+}/SCN^- system fortunately forms a deep red complex with a wavelength of maximum absorbance (λ_{max}) in the visible spectrum. The wavelength setting of 470 nm will be used for absorbance readings for the $FeSCN^{2+}$ complex ion.

A spectrophotometer may be used to measure the absorbance, A, of a solution. Note that absorbance has no units, and is simply a number. The basic law that is applicable in this experiment can be stated as follows: *The absorption of light as it passes through a solution is proportional to the concentration of the absorbing species, the length of the light path, and a fundamental property of the material called the molar absorptivity.*

The *Beer-Lambert Law* states that absorbance depends on three quantities, and can be expressed as:

$$A = \varepsilon \cdot l \cdot c \qquad (5)$$

The molar extinction coefficient or molar absorptivity, ε, has dimensions of L/mole cm. The concentration, c, is in mole/L or M. The path length l is in cm.

The *Beer-Lambert Law* can be written as:

$$A = \varepsilon \cdot l \cdot [FeSCN^{2+}] \qquad (6)$$

this can be rearranged as

$$[FeSCN^{2+}] = A/\varepsilon \cdot l. \tag{7}$$

The total concentration of all ionic forms containing iron is assumed to be either Fe^{3+} or $Fe(SCN)^{2+}$. If we let the amount of iron added to the solution be designated as $[Fe^{3+}]_i$ then

$$[Fe^{3+}]_i = [Fe^{3+}] + [FeSCN^{2+}]. \tag{8}$$

This can be rearrange to solve for $[Fe^{3+}]$:

$$[Fe^{3+}] = [Fe^{3+}]_i - [FeSCN^{2+}], \tag{9}$$

substituting Eq.8 we have

$$[Fe^{3+}] = [Fe^{3+}]_i - A/\varepsilon \cdot l. \tag{10}$$

A similar argument may be made for $[SCN^-]$. This results in the following equation:

$$[SCN^-] = [SCN^-]_i - A/\varepsilon \cdot l. \tag{11}$$

Equations 7, 10,and 11 can be substituted in to Equation 4 to derive the following value for K_{eq}:

$$K_{eq} = \frac{A/\varepsilon \cdot l}{([Fe^{3+}]_i - A/\varepsilon \cdot l)([SCN^-]_i - A/\varepsilon \cdot l)} \tag{12}$$

This equation can be rearranged, and it can be shown that :

$$\frac{A}{[Fe^{3+}]_i [SCN^-]_i} = -\frac{A([Fe^{3+}]_i + [SCN^-]_i) \cdot K_{eq}}{[Fe^{3+}]_i [SCN^-]_i} + \varepsilon \cdot l \cdot K_{eq} \tag{13}$$

Equation 13 takes the form of an equation of a straight line where $y = mx + b$.

If one sets $y = \dfrac{A}{[Fe^{3+}]_i \, [SCN^-]_i}$,

and $x = \dfrac{A\,([Fe^{3+}]_i + [SCN^-]_i)}{[Fe^{3+}]_i \, [SCN^-]_i}$

a graph of the data will give a straight line with a slope = $- K_{eq}$.

Procedure

The solutions in this experiment contain nitric acid. Nitric acid is a corrosive material. Protect your eyes! If an acid solution comes in contact with your skin, rinse with copious amounts of water and notify your laboratory instructor immediately.

Preparation of the KSCN Solution

Use a dispensette pump to add exactly 25.00 mL of 2.0 M nitric acid, HNO_3, to a 100.00 mL volumetric flask.

Carefully, add 10.00 mL of the KSCN stock solution to the volumetric flask containing nitric acid. Record the exact concentration of the stock solution. Add deionized water to dilute the solution to the 100.00 mL mark on the volumetric flask. The bottom of the meniscus should sit on the etched line as shown in Figure 3.1.

Stopper the flask and invert the flask several times to mix the solutions. The new solution now contains 2.00×10^{-4} M KSCN and 0.5 M HNO_3. After it is well mixed, pour the solution into a clean, dry 250 mL beaker.

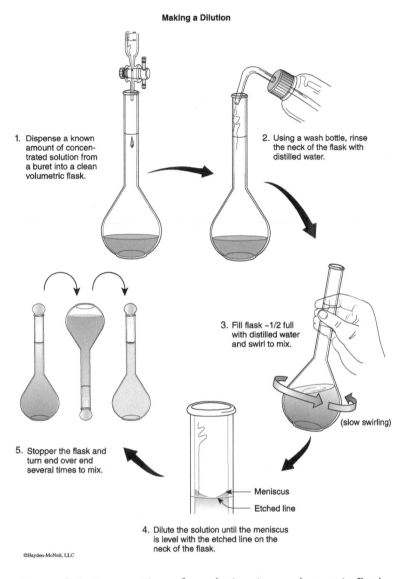

Making a Dilution

1. Dispense a known amount of concentrated solution from a buret into a clean volumetric flask.

2. Using a wash bottle, rinse the neck of the flask with distilled water.

3. Fill flask ~1/2 full with distilled water and swirl to mix.

(slow swirling)

5. Stopper the flask and turn end over end several times to mix.

— Meniscus

— Etched line

4. Dilute the solution until the meniscus is level with the etched line on the neck of the flask.

©Hayden-McNeil, LLC

Figure 3.1 Preparation of a solution in a volumetric flask.

Reaction with Fe(NO₃)₃

Obtain a 25 mL sample of the 0.100 M Fe(NO)₃ stock solution. The solution is 0.100 M Fe(NO₃)₃ in 0.5 M HNO₃.

Use a buret to transfer 1.00 mL of the Fe(NO₃)₃ solution to the beaker containing the KSCN solution. Mix the contents using a stirring rod or a magnetic stir plate.

Measuring the Absorbance

Set the wavelength of to 470 nm, the maximum absorbance for $FeSCN^{2+}$. This wavelength gives the maximum absorbance for our sample solutions.

You will use 0.5 M HNO_3 as your reference. Use a transfer pipet to add the 0.5 M HNO_3 solution to the vial. The vial should be two-thirds full. Use a KimWipe to clean the vial before inserting into the spectrometer. Place the light shield over the sample to prevent light from reaching the detector.

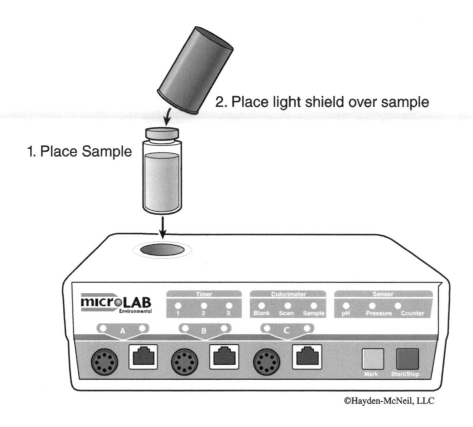

©Hayden-McNeil, LLC

Figure 3.2 Place the sample in the instrument and cover with the light shield.

Use a clean transfer pipet to add a small portion of the reaction solution (KSCN + $Fe(NO_3)_3$ solutions) to the other vial. Record the absorbance of the solution and carefully pour the contents of the vial back into the reaction mixture. Be careful not to spill any of the liquid.

Repeat the previous steps to add another 1.00 mL aliquot of the 0.100M solution of $Fe(NO_3)_3$ to the reaction mixture. Mix well. Remove a small portion of the reaction mixture and measure the absorbance. Continue for a total of ten 1.00 mL additions to the beaker.

Waste Disposal

Place the reaction mixture and any left-over solutions in the waste container. The acid will be neutralized before disposal.

Data Analysis

The creation of a data table in Excel with be the most efficient method of analysis. Create a table that includes the data entries shown below. Enter data for all 10 trials.

Absorbance
$[Fe^{3+}]_i$
$[SCN^-]_i$
$[Fe^{3+}]_i + [SCN^-]$
$[Fe^{3+}]_i [SCN^-]_i$
$A \cdot ([Fe^{3+}]_i + [SCN^-]_i)$
$A/([[Fe^{3+}]_i [SCN^-]_i)$
$A \cdot ([Fe^{3+}]_i + [SCN^-]_i)/([Fe^{3+}]_i [SCN^-]_i)$

Sample calculations for the values of $[Fe^{3+}]_i$ and $[SCN^-]_i$ for trial one are shown below.

The concentration of $[Fe^{3+}]_i$ is:
0.100 M $\cdot$ 1.00 mL/101.00 mL = .0009901 mole/L

Likewise, for $[SCN^-]_i$ the concentration is:
$2.00 \cdot 10^{-4}$ M $\cdot$ 100.00 mL/101.00 mL = .00019802 mole/L

Plotting a Graph

To calculate the equilibrium constant, you must plot a graph where the y-axis corresponds to $A/([Fe^{3+}]_i [SCN^-]_i)$ and the x-axis corresponds to $A \times ([Fe^{3+}]_i + [SCN^-]_i)/([Fe^{3+}]_i [[SCN^-]_i)$.

Construct a graph using the last two data columns. Fit the data to a straight line. The resulting slope with be equal to $-K_{eq}$. The data table and graph should be submitted with your report sheet.

Experiment 3

The Complex Ion Equilibrium of Fe (III) and Thiocyanate Ions

Name: _____

Instructor: _____

Group Members: _____

The data table and graph should be submitted with your report sheet along with copies of your notebook entry.

Questions

1. What is your experimentally determined value for K_{eq}?

2. If the literature value for this equilibrium constant is equal to 150 M^{-2} what is the percent error between the literature value and your experimentally determined value of K_{eq} ?

3. Discuss 3 possible sources of experimental error.

Experiment 4
Borax Solubility

Investigating the Relationship between Thermodynamics and Equilibrium:
Determination of $\Delta H°$, $\Delta S°$, and $\Delta G°$ from Ksp for the dissolution of Borax, a semi-soluble salt

Chemical reactions involve transformations in energy as well as transformations in matter. Thermodynamics is the study of the relationship between heat and other forms of energy. The standard enthalpy change, $\Delta H°$, indicates the amount of heat absorbed or released as a process occurs at constant pressure and under standard conditions. The standard entropy change, $\Delta S°$, indicates the change in disorder in the system as a process occurs under standard conditions. In general, a spontaneous process is favored by an increase in disorder and a release of heat. However, in order to determine whether or not a process will occur in the forward direction under specific conditions, *both* $\Delta H°$ and $\Delta S°$ must be considered. The enthalpy change and the entropy change for a process are combined in the thermodynamic quantity known as standard free energy change or Gibbs free energy, $\Delta G°$.

(1) $\Delta G° = \Delta H° - T\Delta S°$

If $\Delta G°$ is negative, the process will occur in the forward direction at the specified temperature. If $\Delta G°$ is positive, the process will not occur in the forward direction at that temperature; it will be spontaneous in the reverse direction. If $\Delta G°$ is zero, the process is at equilibrium, and there will be not net change in either direction at that temperature. The relationship between the standard free energy change and the equilibrium constant, K, is shown in the following equation.

(2) $\Delta G° = - RT\ln K$

Note that if K is greater than one, then $\Delta G°$ is negative indicating that the process will proceed in the forward direction under the standard conditions.

Combination of the relationships $\Delta G° = \Delta H° - T\Delta S°$ and $\Delta G° = -RT\ln K$ results in the following equation.

(3) $\Delta H° - T\Delta S° = -RT\ln K$

Note: Both $\Delta H°$ and $\Delta S°$ are temperature dependent. However, for the purpose of this exercise it may be assumed that they do not change substantially with temperature. This introduces a degree of error into the results.
Rearranging this equation gives the following.

(4) $\ln K = \dfrac{-\Delta H°}{RT} + \dfrac{\Delta S°}{R}$

A plot of $\ln K$ versus $1/T$ should give a straight line with slope equal to $-\Delta H°/R$. Theoretically, the y intercept of the plot, where $x = 0$, should be equal to $\Delta S°/R$. However, x is $1/T$, and there is no y value for which $1/T = 0$. Thus, $\Delta S°$ may not be determined directly from the plot.

The Relationship between Temperature and Equilibrium: Dissolution of Borax

The thermodynamic quantities $\Delta G°$, $\Delta H°$, and $\Delta S°$ may be determined from equilibrium data by graphing according to equation (4). Consider the semi-soluble salt borax, $Na_2[B_4O_5(OH)_4] \cdot 8H_2O$. Borax is a common household chemical that has a wide range of applications, including use as a laundry detergent and as a roach and ant killer. Borax is one of many salts that are only slightly soluble in water. The dissolution of borax in water is shown by the following equation.

$Na_2[B_4O_5(OH)_4] \cdot 8H_2O(s) \;\rightleftharpoons\; 2\,Na^+(aq) + B_4O_5(OH)_4{}^{2-}(aq) + 8\,H_2O(l)$

The solubility product constant, K_{sp}, for this equation is related to the ion concentrations in the saturated solution as follows.

(5) $K_{sp} = [Na^+]^2[B_4O_5(OH)_4{}^{2-}]$

Note: Recall that K_{sp} is dependent on temperature.

Let x signify the solubility of borax. In a saturated solution, the concentration of tetraborate ion, $B_4O_5(OH)_4^{2-}$, is equal to x and the concentration of sodium ion is equal to 2x. The solubility product expression then becomes as follows.

(6) $K_{sp} = [2x]^2[x] = 4x^3$

The solubility of borax, signified by x, is easily determined by exploiting the weak basicity of the tetraborate anion.

$$B_4O_5(OH)_4^{2-}(aq) + 5 H_2O(l) \rightleftharpoons 4 H_3BO_3(aq) + 2 OH^-(aq)$$

The concentration of $B_4O_5(OH)_4^{2-}$ ion in a saturated solution of borax may be determined by titration with a strong acid according to the following equation.

$$B_4O_5(OH)_4^{2-}(aq) + 2 H^+(aq) + 3 H_2O(l) \rightleftharpoons 4 H_3BO_3(aq)$$

In this experiment, titration will be used to determine the solubility of borax at various temperatures, and K_{sp} at each temperature will be calculated from the solubility using equation (6). The thermodynamic quantities ⬚G°, ⬚H°, and ⬚S° for the dissolution of borax will then be determined by graphing this solubility product data according to equation (4).

Procedure

Label five clean 125 mL Erlenmeyer flasks as 33°C, 36°C, 39°C, 42°C, and 45°C. Add approximately 5 mL of distilled water to each flask, and place them out of the way.

Fill a 600 mL beaker about three quarters full with distilled water. Place the beaker on a hot plate to be heated along with the borax solution. Put an open-mouth graduated pipet into the water.

Measure approximately 18 grams of borax into a 100 mL beaker, and add 50 mL of distilled water. Heat the mixture cautiously on a hot plate while stirring occasionally. Monitor the temperature closely. When the temperature reaches 50°C, observe if there is undissolved salt in the beaker. If there is undissolved borax in the beaker, remove the beaker from the heat and allow it to cool. If all of the borax is completely dissolved at 50°C, add more borax to the beaker while continuing to heat until some of the salt remains undissolved. The solution must be saturated with borax at 50°C. Even after the borax solution has been removed from the hot plate or Bunsen burner, continue to heat the beaker of water with the pipet.

When the borax solution has cooled to ~ 45°C, use the warm, open-mouth pipet to measure a 5 mL aliquot of the solution into the appropriately labeled flask. Try not to allow any undissolved borax to be transferred. Then use the pipet to measure 5 mL of warm distilled water into that aliquot of borax solution, thus rinsing the pipet. Record the actual solution temperature to 0.1°C. Repeat this procedure for each of the five temperatures.

After all of the aliquots have been collected, add an additional 20 mL of distilled water as well as 4 drops of bromocresol green to each flask. The solutions will appear light blue in color. Obtain a 50 mL buret with stand. Fill the buret with the HCl solution in preparation to perform the titration. Record the concentration of the HCl solution. Titrate each borax solution with the standardized HCl solution, recording the initial and final buret readings. The end point is observed when the solution turns from blue to pale yellow.

The thermodynamic quantities may be determined from the data by carrying out the following calculations:

- For each temperature, calculate the number of moles of borax in the 5.00 mL aliquot.
- For each temperature, calculate the concentration of borax in the saturated solution. The concentration of borax is equal to x.
- For each temperature, calculate K_{sp} using the equation $K_{sp} = 4x^3$.
- Plot $\ln(K_{sp})$ versus $1/T$. This should give a straight line.
- Determine $\Delta H°$ from the slope of the line, where slope = $-\Delta H°/R$.
- Determine $\Delta S°$ at one of the five temperatures using the equation $\Delta H° - T\Delta S° = -RT\ln(K_{sp})$.
- Determine $\Delta G°$ at 25°C using the equation $\Delta G° = \Delta H° - T\Delta S°$.

Waste Disposal

The titration solutions may be diluted and rinsed down the sink with cold water. Solid borax should be recovered in a designated waste container.

Name: _____

Instructor: _____

(1) Use Excel to execute the calculations, generate the plot, and carry out linear regression analysis. The data in the spreadsheet should be set up according to the following table.

Beaker label	33°C	36°C	39°C	42°C	45°C
Temperature reading (°C)					
Absolute temperature (K)					
$1/T$					
Buret - final reading					
Buret - initial reading					
Volume of HCl					
Moles of H^+					
Moles of $B_4O_5(OH)_4^{2-}$					
Molarity of $B_4O_5(OH)_4^{2-}$					
K_{sp}					
$\ln(K_{sp})$					

(2)   Report $\Delta H°$, $\Delta S°$ and $\Delta G°$. Show all of your calculations to receive full credit. No points will be awarded if work is not shown.

$\Delta H°$

ΔS°

ΔG°

Post Lab Questions

(1)   Look up the Ksp values for following compounds: lead(II) sulfate, aluminum hydroxide, silver chloride, silver bromide and copper sulfide. Which one is most soluble? least soluble? Explain.

(2)   A student is curious about the Ksp value for NaCl. The student looks up the value in the appendix of his textbook, but can't find a value for NaCl. Why not?

(3)   Explain errors inherent in the experimental design.

(4)   Cite sources of error specific to your data collection.

Experiment 5
Preparation of a Solar Cell

stefano spezi/Shutterstock.com

A photovoltaic cell is a device that converts light energy into electric energy. Common uses of photovoltaic cells include highway signs and communication satellites. You may have used a solar calculator powered by a photovoltaic cell. A series or array of these cells may be combined to create a solar panel.

Photovoltaic cells are composed on semiconductors that pass an electrical current through the cell. Silicon is the most commonly used material for semiconductors.

In this experiment, we will prepare a nanocrystalline dye sensitized solar cell. It will contain a layer of titanium dioxide, TiO_2, that has been stained with a natural dye. The natural dye will absorb light from the sun to produce a flow of electrons.[1-2] The dye molecules absorbed to particles of TiO_2 are sandwiched between two electrodes as shown in Figure 5.1.

When the dye molecules absorb light from the sun, electrons are excited and these electrons are transferred from the dye into the TiO_2.[3] The TiO_2 is a semiconducting material. The electrons flow from the TiO_2 coated electrode to the counter electrode producing electricity.

To continue the cycle, an electrolyte is required. The dye molecule releases electrons when it absorbs light. Those electrons must be replaced by a mediator in order for the solar cell to continue producing electricity. The iodide ion in the electrolyte solution serves as the mediator. When the iodide ion is converted to triiodide, electrons are released. This electron is donated to the dye molecule.

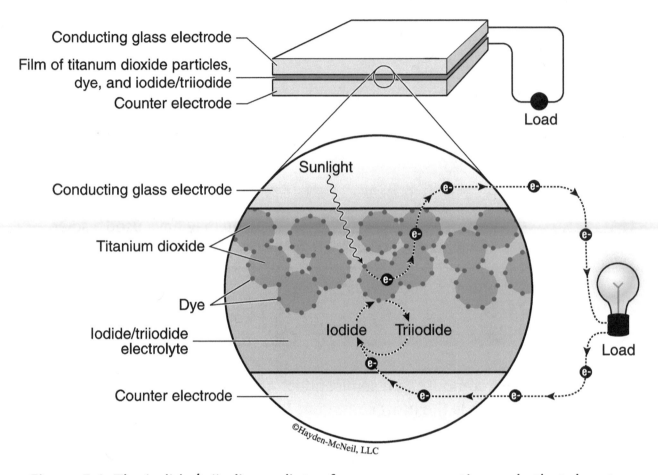

Figure 5.1 The iodide/triiodie mediator forms a regenerative cycle that donates electrons to the dye and then accepts electrons from the counter electrode.

After you prepare your solar cell, you will measure its ability to produce electricity. You will measure the voltage. The voltage is the difference in the energy levels of the TiO_2 and the mediator at the counter electrode. The current measured in amperes is directly proportional to the amount of light or number of photons absorbed by the dye. This will depend on the intensity of the illumination.

The power of the solar cell is the product of the voltage and the current flowing through the load. The unit for power is a watt.

Procedure

Preparing the slides

Obtain two conductive glass plates. Use a multimeter to identify the conducting side of the plate. The multimeter should be set to ohms. You should observe a reading between 10 and 30 ohms. The glass plate has been coated with a thin film of SnO_2, tin oxide.

Place one glass slide on the bench with the conducting side facing upward. Use transparent tape to hold the glass slide in place. Use two strips of tape on each side of the plate, masking no more than 1 mm of the slide. Place a third piece of tape at the top of the slide covering 4-5 mm of the glass slide. Use a Kimwipe wet with ethanol to wipe away any oil or fingerprints.

Preparing the TiO$_2$ Suspension

Add ~ 0.5 gram of nanocrystalline titanium dioxide (TiO_2) to a 100 mL beaker. Add a few drops of acetic acid. Use a glass stirring rod to incorporate the acid and TiO_2. Alternate mixing and the addition of a few drops of acetic acid until the suspension has a smooth consistency, similar to latex paint. You have created a colloidal suspension. If the suspension is too thick, it will be difficult to spread evenly onto the glass slide.

Add one drop of a surfactant (Triton-X 100 or dishwashing detergent.) To avoid the formation of a foam, do not mix or grind after adding the surfactant.

Add a small amount of the titanium dioxide paste to the conductive side of the slide taped to the bench top. As shown in Figure 5.2, quickly spread the paste with a stirring rod or the edge of a clean glass slide. The coating should form a uniform film over the slide.

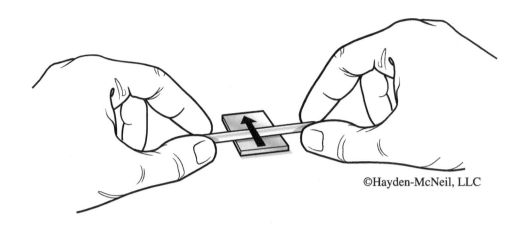

Figure 5.2 Quickly slide the glass rod across the slide to apply a uniform coating of the titanium dioxide suspension.

Carefully remove the tape without scratching the TiO_2 coating. Allow the coating to dry for 1 minute.

Annealing the TiO_2 Coated Slide

Place the coated glass slide on a hotplate under the hood. (The side with the coating should face upward.) The surface will turn brown as the solvent and surfactant dries. The heating process will take 10-20 minutes. The annealing process is finished once the TiO_2 coating turns a brown/purple color and becomes white again. This will occur around 450 °C. (Watch the video for a visual demonstration of what to expect.) Turn off the hotplate and allow the glass to slowly cool. The sample will look quite similar before and after heating. You must observe the darkening stage along the way.

Applying the Anthocyanin Dye

The TiO_2 coated slide will be stained with raspberry juice. Place the coated side of the slide in a watch glass filled with raspberry juice. Gently move the slide to ensure the entire coating is stained by the juice. Use tweezers to remove the slide. Carefully, rinse the slide with deionized water followed by ethanol.

Coating the Counter Electrode

Use tweezers to pass the other glass slide, conducting side down, through a candle flame to coat the conducting side with carbon (soot). For best results, pass the glass piece quickly and repeatedly through the middle part of the flame. (If you are unsure which side is conducting, test again with the multi-meter.) Use a dry cotton swab to wipe away the soot from three sides of the slide.

Assembling the Solar Cell

Place the TiO_2 coated slide on the bench with the coating facing up. Place the soot covered slide face down on top of the TiO_2 coating as seen in Figure 5.3. Basically, you will assemble the two glass plates with coated sides together, but offset so that uncoated glass extends beyond the sandwich. The uncoated glass will later be attached to the alligator clips of the multimeter. Do not rub or slide the plates. Clamp the plates together with binder clips.

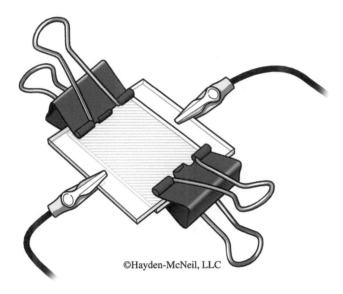

©Hayden-McNeil, LLC

Figure 5.3 The two glass plates are offset so that the uncoated portions of the slides is exposed and attached to the alligator clamps.

71

Applying the Electrolyte Solution

The KI_3 electrolyte solution consists of 0.5 M KI and 0.05 M I_2 in anhydrous ethylene glycol. Add a drop of a triiodide solution to opposite edges of the plate. Capillary action will cause the KI_3 solution to travel between the two plates. Use a tissue to wipe away any excess electrolyte.

Measuring the Electrical Output

Take your solar cell outside in the sunlight. Connect a multi-meter by attaching an alligator clip to each plate. The negative electrode is the TiO_2 coated glass and the positive electrode is the carbon (soot) coated glass. Place the slide with the TiO_2 coating toward the sun. Test the current and voltage produced by solar illumination. Place a piece of paper over the solar cell to see the voltage drop when the energy source is blocked.

After reading the procedure, please watch the following video:

https://www.youtube.com/watch?v=Jw3qCLOXmi0

References

(1) Smestad, G. *J. Chem Educ.* **1998**, *75*, 752.

(2) Smestad, G.P.; Bignozzi, C; Argazzi, R. S*olar Energy Materials and Solar Cells*, vol 32, **1994**, 259-273.

(3) http://education.mrsec.wisc.edu/289.htm

(4) Smedstad, G.; Huseth, A.; Shanks, K.; Bruecken, P.; Goates, W. *Nanocrystalline Solar Cell Kit*, University of Wisconsin Board of Regents, **1998**.

Report Sheet

Experiment 5
Solar Cell

Name: _____

Instructor: _____

(1) Did your solar cell conduct electricity? What were the current and voltage readings?

(2) How much power did your solar cell produce?

(3) What area of solar cell would be needed to produce 1 watt? (Assume the voltage produced is constant and that the current would be proportional to the area of the solar cell.)

(4) How does the nanocrystalline dye sensitized solar cell resemble the natural process of photosynthesis?

(5) What is the compound found in raspberries that plays a role in our solar cell? Draw the structure for the compound.

(6) In our solar cell, an organic compound chelates with TiO_2. Define chelation and draw the chelated structure.

(7) In our system, the iodide ion in the electrolyte acts as a mediator. What is the role of the mediator? What is the formula for the mediator in the oxidized state? in the reduced state?

(8) The conversion efficiency of the solar cell is the maximum electrical power output divided by the incoming solar power on the same area. How could you improve the efficiency of your solar cell?

(9) Name two other common uses of TiO_2.

Online Activities & Experiments

Chem 1212L/1312L /1412L

Online Experiment 1
Analysis of Acetic Acid in Vinegar

An Acid-Base Titration

Household vinegar is a solution of acetic acid, CH_3COOH. Typically, commercial vinegar contains 5-6 % acetic acid. By neutralizing the acetic acid with a base, we can quantify the amount of acetic acid in a sample of vinegar.

$$CH_3COOH(aq) \quad + \quad NaOH(aq) \quad \rightarrow \quad NaOOCCH_3(aq) \quad + \quad + \quad H_2O(l)$$

Procedure

The exact concentration of the NaOH must be known. The NaOH has already been standardized using KHP, potassium hydrogen phthalate, as a primary standard. Record the exact concentration of the NaOH solution.

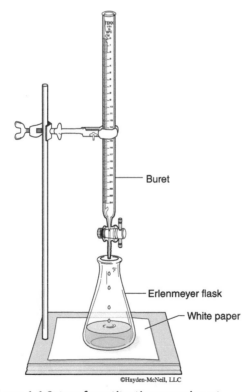

Buret

Erlenmeyer flask

White paper

©Hayden-McNeil, LLC

Figure 1.1 Set up for a titration experiment.

Phenolphthalein will serve as a color indicator. Phenolphthalein is colorless in the presence of acid and will turn pink when basic conditions are detected. You will observe the end point of the titration just after the acid has been consumed by the titrant. When one extra drop of base is added to the flask, the solution will turn pink.

Rinse a 50.00 mL buret with distilled water. Follow by rinsing with a small portion (~5mL) of NaOH. After rinsing, fill the buret to the 0.0 mL mark. Set up the buret as shown in Figure 1.1.

Next, use a volumetric pipet to transfer exactly 5.00 mL of vinegar into an Erlenmeyer flask. Add ~10 mL of distilled water to this flask followed by 3-4 drops of phenolphthalein indicator to the solution in the flask.

Titrate with the NaOH solution, recording the initial and final buret readings. The buret should be read to the hundredth's place. Swirl the flask contents to ensure complete mixing.

WASTE DISPOSAL: All solutions may be rinsed down the sink with cold water.

Online
Experiment 2
The Rate of Decolorization

The Green Fades Away

This experiment will study the kinetics of a reaction involving a green dye. Upon reacting with a Lewis base, the dye undergoes structural changes that cause the molecule in solution to convert from a green color to colorless.

Before measuring how quickly the color disappears, let us consider why the molecule has color. Dyes are aromatic organic compounds. An *aromatic compound* contains planar ring systems with alternating double bonds. The conjugated compound gains chemical stability from the delocalization of electrons in the ring system, as seen in benzene, C_6H_6. The electrons are not associated with a single atom or one covalent bond. Instead, delocalized pi electrons form an orbital cloud that extends over several adjacent atoms.

Specifically, a *chromophore* is the part of a molecule responsible for its color. The color arises when a molecule absorbs certain wavelengths of visible light as an electron is excited from its ground state to a higher energy level.[1] In conjugated chromophores, the electrons jump between energy levels that are extended pi orbitals, created by a series of alternating single and double bonds.[2]

The parent dye does not contain any methyl groups. This structure is called *pararosanline* and is a red color.

When four methyl groups are added, the dye appears a reddish purple as seen in *methyl violet*.

As more methyl groups are added, the color appears blue, as is the case in crystal violet with six methyl groups.

Finally, methyl green displays a green color with seven methyl groups attached.

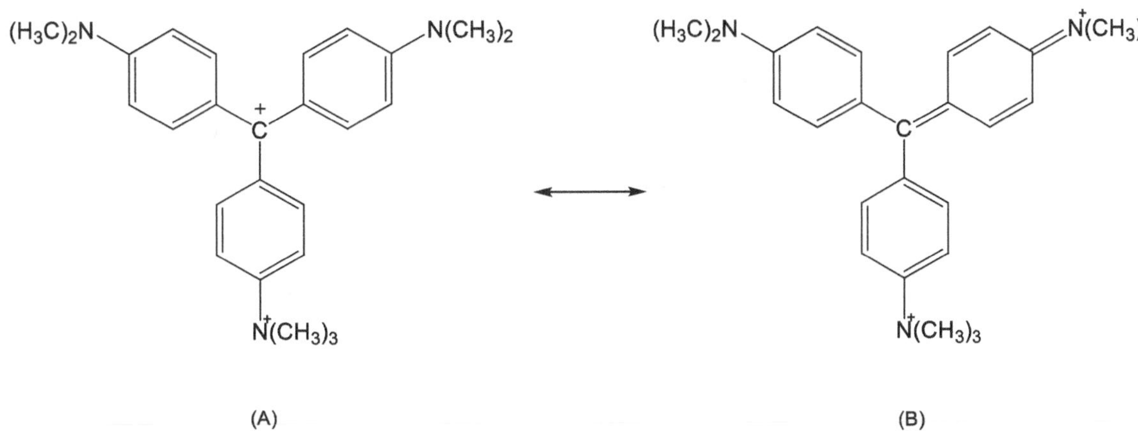

Figure 2.1 Two resonance structures of methyl green.

The structure of methyl green can be illustrated with resonance structures.[2] As seen in Figure 2.1 (A), the central carbon atom can bear a positive charge. It can act as a Lewis acid. This means it will act as an electron-pair acceptor and react with a Lewis base to form an adduct. The carbon atom will share the electron pair furnished by the Lewis base.

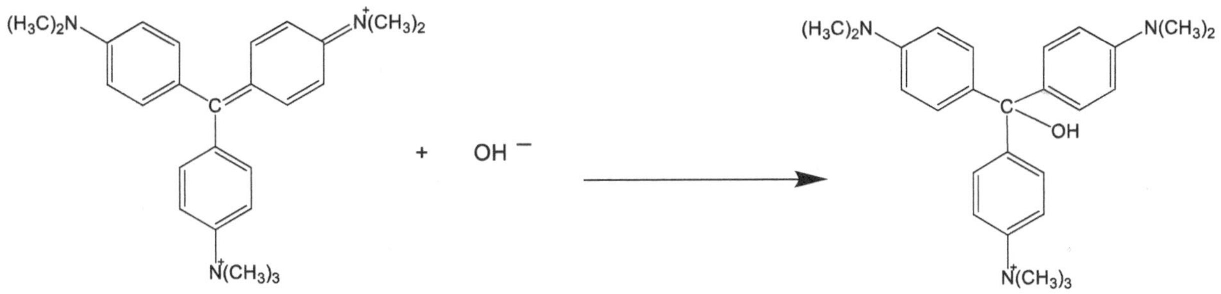

Figure 2.2 The reaction of methyl green with hydroxide ion.

When a Lewis base such as a hydroxide ion adds to the central carbon in methyl green, the central atom will now have four single bonds as shown in Figure 2.2. The geometry around the central atom converts from trigonal planar to tetrahederal. The tetrahedral geometry does not allow pi bonding. The color of the dye will disappear because electron delocalization no longer exists over the entire molecule.

The color of the methyl green solution fades under basic conditions. The rate of the reaction is faster as the conditions become more basic. In the experiment, we will mix solutions of 2.0×10^{-4} M methyl green with basic buffer solutions. We will use 0.040 M aqueous solutions of a Na_2HPO_4 and Na_3PO_4 buffer system. The buffer generates an OH^- ion that reactions with methyl green.

$$PO_4^{3-} + H_2O \rightleftharpoons HPO_4^{2-} + OH^-$$

The equilibrium expression can be written:

$$K_b = \frac{[HPO_4^{2-}][OH^-]}{[PO_4^{3-}]} = 4.5 \times 10^{-2}$$

By rearranging the equation, you can determine the concentration of OH^-. It is important to note that the actual concentration of the buffer ions is not important. It is their relative concentrations that matter.

$$[OH^-] = 4.5 \times 10^{-2} \times \frac{[PO_4^{3-}]}{[HPO_4^{2-}]}$$

The reaction is first order with respect to the dye. When the concentration of the dye doubles, the rate also doubles. The observed rate law is:

$$rate = k_1 [dye][H_2O] + k_2[dye][OH^-]$$

The reaction acts as if it were first order when the concentrations of both H_2O and OH^- are much greater than the concentration of the dye. For our reaction, the concentration of methyl green dye will be 1.0×10^{-4} M. Thus, $[H_2O] >> [dye]$ and $[OH^-] >> [dye]$. Under these conditions, the concentration of H_2O and OH^- essentially remain constant and the reaction is called pseudo-first order. We can write an observed rate constant that includes the quantities of $[H_2O]$ and $[OH^-]$.

$$k_{obs} = k_1 [H_2O] + k_2[OH^-]$$

By substituting the observed rate constant into the original rate equation, we obtain this equation:

$$\text{rate} = k_{obs}[\text{dye}]$$

Integrating the new equation yields: $\qquad \ln[\text{dye}] = -k_{obs}\,t + \ln[\text{dye}]_o \qquad (6)$

The Beer-Lambert Law states the relationships between absorbance and concentration: $A = \varepsilon\,\ell\,c$. This allows us to write the concentration of the dye in terms of absorbance:

$$[\text{dye}] = A/\varepsilon\ell \qquad (7)$$

The molar absorptivity, ε, and the cell pathlength, ℓ, are constant during the experiment. By substituting equation 7 into equation 6, the integrated rate law can be rewritten:

$$\ln(A/\varepsilon\ell) = -k_{obs}t + \ln(A/\varepsilon\ell)$$

$$\text{or} \quad \ln A - \ln(\varepsilon\ell) = -k_{obs}t + \ln A_o - \ln(\varepsilon\ell)$$

$$\text{or} \quad -\ln A = k_{obs}t - \ln A_o$$

Therefore, we can determine the rate constant of the reaction by plotting the negative value of the natural logarithm of the absorbance, $-\ln A$, versus time. The slope of the graph is the rate constant, k_{obs}.

Procedure

Use the MicroLab software to select a wavelength of 590nm.

Trial	0.040M Na$_3$PO$_4$ (mL)	0.040M Na$_2$HPO$_4$ (mL)
1	5.0	10.0
2	7.0	8.0
3	8.0	7.0
4	10.0	5.0

Use a pipet or dispensette pump to add the exact volumes of the 0.040M Na$_3$PO$_4$ and 0.040M Na$_2$HPO$_4$ as shown for the first trial listed in the table shown above. Pipet carefully to add exact amounts. Swirl the contents to mix the solutions. Now, prepare to act quickly because the reaction occurs rapidly. Add 5.0 mL of the methyl green solution. Swirl to mix. Rinse the cuvette by filling it with solution and pouring the contents back into the beaker. Now, fill the cuvette and place it in the spectrophotometer. Be careful to align the cuvette properly in the spectrophotometer.

Immediately start recording time and read the absorbance of the solution. Continue to take an absorbance reading every 15 seconds until the absorbance value drops below 0.20. You should have a minimum of five data points for time versus absorbance. Follow the same procedure for every trial.

References

1. http://goldbook.iupac.org/PDF/goldbook.pdf

2. http://stainsfile.info/StainsFile/dyes/dyecolor.htm

3. http://stainsfile.info/StainsFile/dyes/42585.htm

Synthesis & Analysis of a Copper Coordination Compound

During this experiment, you will synthesize a coordination compound. A coordination compound forms when a central metal atom is surrounded by one or more ligands. A ligand is an atom or molecule that donates electrons to the metal center. The image below illustrates a metal coordinating with the non-bonding electrons on the ligand. A bond forms when a ligand acts as a Lewis base and donates two electrons to the electron deficient metal. The transition metal is acting as a Lewis acid. Hemoglobin, vitamin B_{12} and chlorophyll are examples of coordination compounds found in nature. Coordination compounds are also developed for industrial applications such as catalysts.

You will synthesize a copper containing coordination compound and later analyze the compound to determine its empirical formula.[1] Based on the starting reagents, we know the compound will contain copper (II), ammonia, sulfate ion and water. Your task is to determine the mole ratio of each component. The general formula is $Cu_x(NH_3)_y(SO_4)_z \cdot H_2O$. The ammonia serves as a ligand and the sulfate acts as a counter ion. The water molecule is incorporated into the crystal lattice of the solid compound. The water is not bonding to the metal center. It is simply a water of hydration.

Synthesis

Copper (II) sulfate pentahydrate will be dissolved in water. Once dissolved, the copper 2+ ion is surrounded by six water molecules to form $[Cu(H_2O)_6]^{2+}$. The six water molecules act as neutral ligands. Once concentrated ammonia is added to the solution, NH_3 ligands begin to displace the covalently bound water molecules and a dramatic color change occurs. The product has the general formula of $Cu_x(NH_3)_y(SO_4)_z \cdot H_2O$.

Gravimetric Analysis of Sulfate

The amount of sulfate in your product can be determined with gravimetric analysis. The compound is water-soluble. The sulfate ion can be precipitated out of solution using an aqueous solution of barium chloride. A metathesis reaction should form solid $BaSO_4$ that can be isolated and measured to determine the original sulfate content.

$$Ba^{2+}(aq) + SO_4^{2-}(aq) \rightarrow BaSO_4(s)$$

Volumetric Analysis of Ammonia

The ammonia content of the product can be analyzed by an acid-base titration. This is a strong acid-weak base titration. Methyl orange will be used as the color indicator.

$$NH_3(aq) + HCl \rightarrow NH_4^+(aq)$$

Spectrophotometric Analysis of Cu^{2+} ion

The coordination compound is intensely colored. The color is created by the Cu^{2+} ion. When dissolved in water, Cu^{2+} ions have a maximum absorbance around 660nm. None of the other components in the coordination compound absorbs visible light. No absorbance can be attributed to NH_3, SO_4^{2-} or H_2O. The color and thus the absorbance observed can be used as a measure of the Cu^{2+} concentration.

You may recall the Beer Lambert law that states: *The absorption of light as it passes through a solution is proportional to the concentration of the absorbing species, the length of the light path and a fundamental property of the material called the molar absorptivity.* The concentration of a solution is directly proportional to its absorbance. We will create a calibration plot using solutions of known Cu^{2+} concentration to determine the concentration of Cu^{2+} in the coordination compound.

Part I: Synthesis of Coordination Complex

Place ~5 grams of copper (II) sulfate pentahydrate, $CuSO_4 \cdot 5H_2O$, in a 250 mL beaker and record the exact mass of the starting material. Add ~15 mL of deionized water. Next, add 10.00 mL of 15 M NH_3 to the beaker and stir the solution under the hood. ***Caution: concentrated ammonia is extremely caustic. If ammonia makes contact with your skin, rinse with copious amounts of water and contact your instructor immediately.***

Obtain 10.00 mL of 95% ethanol in a small beaker. Use a pipet to add the ethanol to the solution. Add dropwise over a one-minute period. Stir and allow the solution to cool to room temperature.

In a small clean beaker, prepare a solution that contains 10 mL of concentrated ammonia and 10 mL of 95 % ethanol. Cover the beaker with a watch glass and place under the hood. This solution will be used to rinse the crystals of your product.

Set up a Buchner funnel for vacuum filtration. <u>Pre-weigh a watch glass and filter paper.</u> Isolate your crystals using vacuum filtration. Turn off the vacuum and carefully pour 10 mL the ammonia –ethanol solution onto the crystals. Use a spatula to break up any clumps. Turn on the vacuum to remove the wash.

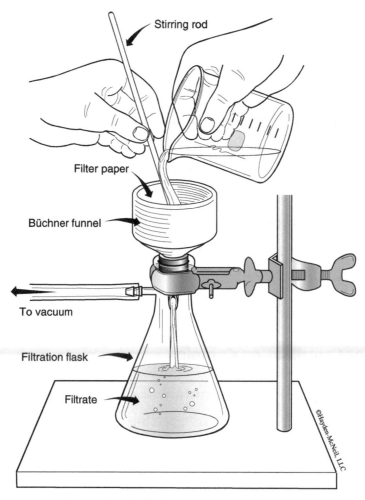

Stirring rod

Filter paper

Büchner funnel

To vacuum

Filtration flask

Filtrate

©Hayden-McNeil LLC

Separation Technique: Suction Filtration

Repeat the washing procedure one more time with the remaining 10 mL of the ammonia-ethanol solution. Use an ethanol wash bottle to rinse the crystals with 95% ethanol, again breaking up any clumps. Finally, wash the crystals with 10 mL of acetone. Allow air to flow through the funnel to ensure all of the solvent is removed. This may take 15-20 minutes for the crystals to dry completely. Transfer your crystals to the watch glass, removing the moist filter paper and discarding it in the waste container. Record the mass of the watch glass product. Determine the mass contribution from your product.

On particularly humid or rainy days, it may not be possible to record the mass of your dry product. The product may need to be placed in a desiccator to dry before continuing the analysis.

Part II: Analysis of Product

You and your lab partner will work with another pair to complete the analyses needed to determine the components of the coordination compound and determine its empirical formula. You must determine x, y and z for the formula, $Cu_x(NH_3)_y(SO_4)_z \cdot H_2O$.

Gravimetric Analysis of Sulfate

Place ~ 1 gram of your product in a 150 mL beaker. Record the actual mass of the coordination compound. Dissolve the solid in ~ 10 mL of 6M HNO_3, nitric acid. *Caution: nitric acid is caustic. If any acid encounters your skin, notify your TA immediately and rinse with copious amounts of water.*

Obtain 5-6 mL of 1 M $BaCl_2$. Use a pipet to add the solution dropwise. Record your observations. Continue to add the 1 M $BaCl_2$ solution until precipitation is complete.

<u>Pre-weigh a watch glass and piece of filter paper</u>. Record the mass.

Set up a Buchner funnel. Use vacuum filtration to collect the barium sulfate precipitate. For accurate results, you must be sure that all of the sulfate has precipitated. After filtering the solid, pour the filtrate in a small beaker. Test the filtrate for unreacted sulfate ion. Add a few drops of 1 M $BaCl_2$. If precipitation is observed, add an additional 1 mL of 1 M $BaCl_2$ and refilter.

Rinse the filtered precipitate with ~ 5 mL of deionized water and finally, rinse with ~10 mL of acetone. Allow air to flow through the funnel to dry the precipitated barium sulfate, $BaSO_4$.

Repeat a second trial with another 1 gram sample of your product.

Calculate the mass percent of SO_4^{2-} for each trial.

Waste: Place the waste from this test in the bottle labeled "barium waste."

Volumetric Analysis of NH₃

Place ~1 gram of the coordination compound in a 250 mL Erlenmeyer flask. Record the exact mass of the compound. Dissolve the solid in 30 mL of deionized water. Add 10 drops of methyl orange indicator. Titrate the solution with HCl. Record the concentration of the standardized HCl solution.

Methyl orange changes from orange-yellow to red at pH ~ 3.5-4. The blue color from the copper 2+ ions will impact the colors observed throughout the titration. The solution is initially a deep blue. It will become a blue-green color then pea-green. When ~85% of the needed acid has been added, the solution is a golden yellow. You will observe a pumpkin-orange color at the endpoint. A red-orange solution indicates that the titration is passed the endpoint.

Repeat a second trial with another 1 gram sample of your product.

Use the stoichiometric ratio between ammonia and HCl in the neutralization reaction to determine the amount of ammonia in the compound.

Spectrophotometric Analysis of Copper (II)

Prepare a calibration plot by using the standards listed below. Use a buret to dispense the exact volumes of stock solution and ammonia. Record the concentration of the Cu^{2+} stock solution.

Test Tube	Cu^{2+} stock solution	1 M HNO_3
1	0.0 mL	10.00 mL
2	2.0 mL	8.00 mL
3	4.0 mL	6.00 mL
4	6.0 mL	4.00 mL
5	8.0 mL	2.00 mL
6	10.0 mL	0.00 mL

The first sample will be used as the reference for the remainder of the samples. The solution is colorless and should give an absorbance reading of 0. Thoroughly mix the contents of each test tube before measuring the absorbance at 635 nm.

Graph the absorbance versus concentration and use linear regression to fit the data to a straight line. You will use this equation to determine the concentration of Cu^{2+} in your sample.

Studying your compound: You will prepare two samples of your coordination compound for spectrophotometric analysis.

Add 0.2 grams of your compound to a small, dry beaker. Record the exact mass of your sample. Transfer exactly 10.00 mL of 1 M HNO_3 to the beaker and mix thoroughly. Transfer a portion of the solution to a cuvette and measure the absorbance. Use 1M HNO_3 as your reference. From this value, you can determine the molar concentration. Repeat the analysis with another 0.2 g sample of your compound. Again, record the exact mass of your sample.

Empirical Formula: Determination of x, y and z in $Cu_x(NH_3)_y(SO_4)_z \cdot H_2O$

Use the experimental data to determine the empirical formula based on the mass percent of Cu^{2+}, sulfate ion and NH_3.

Reference

(1) Williams,G. M; Olmstead, J. and Breska, A.P. *J. Chem Educ.* **1989**, *66*, 1043-1045.

An ionic compound is often described as being soluble or insoluble in water. We can more carefully examine the degree of solubility by writing an equilibrium expression for the dissolution of the ionic compound. We learned from the solubility rules that AgCl, silver chloride, is not soluble in water. We can write an equilibrium expression and a solubility product constant, K_{sp}. The K_{sp} for this equation is related to the ion concentrations in the saturated solution as follows:

$$AgCl(s) \rightleftharpoons Ag^+(aq) + Cl^-(aq)$$

$$Ksp = [Ag^+][Cl^-]$$

Solubility product constants are used to describe saturated solutions of ionic compounds with relatively low solubility. A saturated solution is in a state of dynamic equilibrium between the dissolved, dissociated, ionic compound and the undissolved solid. When the K_{sp} value is known, we can calculate the molar solubility of a compound. For example, the K_{sp} value for AgCl is 1.77×10^{-10} which gives a molar solubility value of 1.33×10^{-5}.

$$K_{sp} = [x][x] = x^2$$

In this experiment, we will calculate K_{sp} for an ionic compound with low solubility in water.[1] We will also observe the common ion effect. *In general, the solubility of an ionic compound is lower in a solution containing a common ion than in pure water.* This is in agreement with Le Chatelier's principle. For example, if AgCl(s) is dissolved in sea water, the solution already contains Cl⁻ ions before AgCl(s) is added. The common ion, Cl⁻(aq), will cause the equilibrium to shift to the left and thus lower the solubility.

Procedure

Record the mass of a clean, dry 250 mL Erlenmeyer flask. Add ~5 g of $Ba(NO_3)_2$ to the beaker and reweigh, recording the exact mass. Next, use a graduated cylinder to add 50.0 mL of distilled water to the flask. Stir the contents for 10 minutes. Measure the temperature of the solution. Carefully, decant the solution into a beaker and save the solid that remains in the flask. Place the flask on the hotplate and evaporate to dryness. Use tongs to remove the flask from the hot plate. Allow the flask to cool to room temperature and record the mass of the flask and its contents. Discard the barium nitrate solid and liquid waste into the designated waste containers. Barium nitrate is toxic if ingested. To reduce the hazardous waste generated from this experiment, you will collect data from two other groups instead of completing three trials.

The Common Ion Effect

Use a clean, dry flask to repeat the procedure dissolving the $Ba(NO_3)_2$ in 50.0 mL of 0.5 M HNO_3 instead of distilled water. Again, discard the waste into designated containers. Collect data from two other groups for comparison.

References

(1) Wruck, B.; Reinstein, J. *J. Chem Educ.* **1989**, *66*,515-6.

A neutralization reaction is a chemical reaction between an acid and a base to form a salt and water. It may be interpreted as a proton transfer reaction where a proton (H^+) is transferred from the acid to the base. In this context, an acid is considered a proton donor based on the Bronsted – Lowry definition. A common example of a neutralization reaction is the reaction between sodium hydroxide and hydrochloric acid.

$$NaOH(aq) \; + \; HCl(aq) \longrightarrow H_2O(l) \; + \; NaCl(aq)$$

Acids are important compounds found throughout nature. The tart flavor of citrus fruits is caused by the presence of citric acid. Lactic acid is present in sour milk. Vinegar, often used in food preparation, is an aqueous solution of acetic acid. The sting of an ant bite is caused by formic acid. These are just a few examples of acids that you may encounter in daily life.

Acids are characterized as being strong or weak, depending on the extent of ionization of the acid in aqueous solution. A strong acid, such as hydrochloric acid, ionizes essentially completely in aqueous solution.

$$HCl(aq) \; + \; H_2O(l) \longrightarrow Cl^{1-}(aq) \; + \; H_3O^+(aq)$$

A weak acid, such as acetic acid, only ionizes to a small extent in aqueous solution. The molecular form of the weak acid is in equilibrium with the ions formed.

$$HC_2H_3O_2(aq) \ + \ H_2O(l) \ \rightleftharpoons \ C_2H_3O_2^-(aq) \ + \ H_3O^+(aq)$$

Because ionization of the weak acid results in an equilibrium situation, an equilibrium constant expression can be written to relate the equilibrium constant for the reaction (referred to as the acid ionization constant, K_a) to the equilibrium concentrations of the different species.

$$K_a = \frac{[C_2H_3O_2^{1-}][H_3O^{1+}]}{[HC_2H_3O_2]}$$

The relative magnitude of K_a indicates the relative strength of the acid. In general, the **larger the K_a**, the greater the extent of ionization and the **stronger the acid**.

A technique commonly used to determine the extent of ionization and K_a for a weak acid is pH titration. This technique involves monitoring the pH of a solution of the acid while adding a base solution of known concentration. Consider the titration curve shown in the figure below. A 20.0 mL sample of 0.1000 M weak acid was titrated with a standard solution of 0.1000 M NaOH.

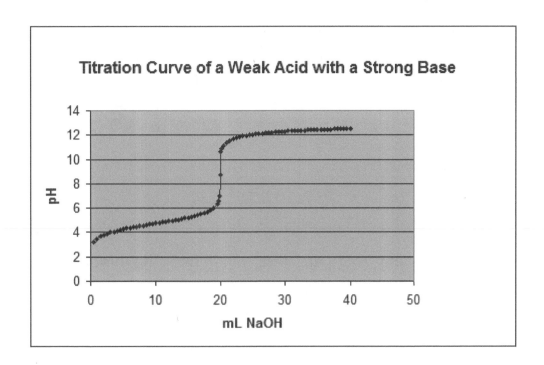

This curve shows the change in pH of the solution as base is added. Recall that pH is an indication of the hydronium ion concentration in the solution and expressed as pH = – log[H₃O⁺]. The chemical reaction can be represented by the following equation where HA represents the weak acid.

$$NaOH(aq) + HA(aq) \longrightarrow H_2O(l) + NaA(aq)$$

The initial pH is low, which is characteristic of an acid. As the first drops of base solution are added, the pH does not change drastically. The added base is "consumed" through the reaction to form water and the salt, NaA. The region of greatest pH change is seen close to the equivalence point. The **equivalence point** is the point of the titration where a stoichiometric amount of base has been added. This means just enough base has been added to completely react with all of the acid present. At this point, the HA has been transformed into A⁻. At the equivalence point, the solution is essentially an aqueous solution of the salt, NaA. Consequently, the equivalence point for titration of a weak acid with a strong base will occur at a pH above 7 because the salt of a weak acid and a strong base gives a basic solution. After the equivalence point has been reached, the pH becomes quite high due to the presence of excess base.

The data from the titration curve can be used to determine the K_a and extent of ionization for the weak acid. For a generic weak acid, HA, the ionization equation is written

$$HA(aq) \ + \ H_2O(l) \ \rightleftharpoons \ A^-(aq) \ + \ H_3O^+(aq)$$

$$K_a = \frac{[A^-][H_3O^+]}{[HA]}$$

The concentrations $[A^-]$ and $[H_3O^+]$ are determined from the *initial* pH.

$$pH = -\log[H_3O^+] \quad so \quad [H_3O^+] = 10^{-pH}$$

According to the ionization equation, A^- and H_3O^+ are present in a 1:1 mole ratio. Therefore, $[A^-] = [H_3O^+]$.

The concentration of HA, M_A, is determined from the titration data at the equivalence point. The following equation can be used.

$$M_A = \frac{M_B V_B}{V_A}$$
where M_B = molar concentration of the base
V_B = volume of base added at the equivalence point
V_A = initial volume of acid used
*Note: This equation can only be used when the acid and base react in a 1:1 mole ratio.

The concentration given by M_A does not take into consideration the ionization of the acid. Therefore, the equilibrium concentration of HA, $[HA]$, is less than M_A: $[HA] = M_A - [H_3O^{1+}]$. However, under the conditions of this experiment, the extent of ionization of the acid is small and can be neglected.

Thus, K_a can be determined from the initial pH and the equivalence point data as follows.

$$K_a = \frac{[A^-][H_3O^+]}{[HA]} \quad = \quad \frac{[H_3O^+]^2}{M_A - [H_3O^+]} \quad \cong \quad \frac{(10^{-pH})^2}{M_A}$$

The extent of ionization can be interpreted as the fraction of acid molecules that have ionized in the solution. The extent of ionization is calculated as follows.

$$\text{extent of ionization} = \frac{[A^-]}{M_A} \cong \frac{[H_3O^+]}{M_A}$$

The extent of ionization is often written as a percentage.

$$\% \text{ ionization} = \frac{[H_3O^+]}{M_A} \times 100$$

The acid ionization constant can also be estimated directly from the titration curve. Refer to the figure of the titration curve. Initially, HA is present. At the equivalence point, the HA has been transformed into A^-. Halfway between the initial point and the equivalence point, half of the HA has been transformed into A^-, and the concentration of HA is equal to the concentration of A^-. A solution that contains a weak acid and its conjugate base acts as a buffer solution and can be described according to the Henderson - Hasselbalch equation.

$$pH = pK_a + \log \frac{[A^-]}{[HA]} \qquad \text{where } pK_a = -\log K_a$$

At the halfway point, $[A^-] = [HA]$, so $pH_{1/2} = pK_a + \log(1)$. Since $\log(1)$ is zero, the following relationships exist.

$$pH_{1/2} = pK_a \qquad \text{or} \qquad [H_3O^+]_{1/2} = K_a$$

Thus, the K_a can be estimated by determining the hydronium ion concentration halfway between the initial point and the equivalence point.

The purpose of this experiment is to determine the K_a and percent ionization for acetic acid by titrating a vinegar solution. The concentration of the acetic acid in the vinegar solution will also be determined for comparison. Normally, vinegar solutions contain ~ 5% acetic acid.

Procedure

Calibrate the pH electrode according to the instructions provided in the lab. **The electrode tip must be immersed in a buffer solution when not in use for the experiment.** Do not let the tip of the electrode dry out. Rinse the electrode with deionized water and wipe with a soft tissue before placing the electrode in a different solution.

Setting up the dispenser and counter

1. Attach the drop dispenser and drop counter to the ring stand. Place a beaker under the counter in order to catch the drops. Fill the dispenser with the titrant, NaOH.

   Caution: NaOH is caustic and may cause severe burns if not handled properly. If the NaOH solution comes in contact with your skin, rinse the affected area with cold water and notify your instructor immediately.

2. Align the dispenser to release a drop through the notch in the drop counter. DO NOT OBSCURE THE COUNTER WITH THE DISPENSER APPARATUS.

3. Start a slow stream of drops through the dispenser. Ensure that these are triggering the drop counter. If they are, the red light on the counter will blink each time a drop is detected.

4. Stop the droplet stream and empty the container.

Use a 20.00 mL volumetric pipet to transfer 20.00 mL of vinegar into a 250 mL beaker. Place a stir bar in the beaker and place the beaker on top of the stir plate. While stirring, carefully immerse the electrode into the vinegar solution. Do not let the stir bar hit or harm the tip of the electrode. Continue to monitor the electrode as the titration proceeds.

The electrode tip must be immersed in a buffer solution when not in use for the experiment. Do not let the tip of the electrode dry out. Rinse the electrode with deionized water and wipe with a soft tissue before placing the electrode in a different solution.

Next, follow the instructions to connect the drop counter to the MicroLab system. This allows MicroLab to recognize the drop counter as a sensor.

Data Analysis

Prepare a graph of pH versus volume of base added. Indicate the equivalence point on the graph. Combine the molarity of the base with the volume used to reach the equivalence point to find the concentration of acetic acid (vinegar) in the beverage.

Find the pH of the halfway point on the graph to determine a value of K_a for acetic acid. Compare this value to the literature value. Now calculate the K_a from the initial pH and the equivalence point data. Compare this value of K_a with the literature value. Find the percent ionization of the phosphoric acid in the beverage.

Exp. No.	Experiment/Subject		Date	01
Name	Lab Partner		Locker/ Desk No.	Course & Section No.

Signature	Date	Witness/TA	Date

Exp. No.	Experiment/Subject		Date	01
Name	Lab Partner		Locker/ Desk No.	Course & Section No.

Signature	Date	Witness/TA		Date

02

Exp. No.	Experiment/Subject		Date	
Name	Lab Partner		Locker/ Desk No.	Course & Section No.

Signature		Date	Witness/TA		Date

THE HAYDEN-McNEIL STUDENT LAB NOTEBOOK

Note: Insert Divider Under Copy Sheet Before Writing

Exp. No.	Experiment/Subject		Date	
Name	Lab Partner		Locker/ Desk No.	Course & Section No.

Signature		Date	Witness/TA		Date

Exp. No.	Experiment/Subject		Date	
Name	Lab Partner		Locker/Desk No.	Course & Section No.

Signature		Date	Witness/TA		Date

Exp. No.	Experiment/Subject		Date	
Name	Lab Partner		Locker/ Desk No.	Course & Section No.

Signature	Date	Witness/TA		Date

Note: Insert Divider Under Copy Sheet Before Writing

Exp. No.	Experiment/Subject		Date	
Name	Lab Partner		Locker/ Desk No.	Course & Section No.

Signature		Date	Witness/TA		Date

Exp. No.	Experiment/Subject		Date	
Name	Lab Partner		Locker/ Desk No.	Course & Section No.

Signature		Date	Witness/TA		Date

Exp. No.	Experiment/Subject		Date	
Name	Lab Partner		Locker/ Desk No.	Course & Section No.

Signature		Date	Witness/TA		Date

Note: Insert Divider Under Copy Sheet Before Writing

Exp. No.	Experiment/Subject		Date	05
Name	Lab Partner		Locker/ Desk No.	Course & Section No.

COPY

Signature	Date	Witness/TA		Date

Exp. No.	Experiment/Subject		Date	
Name		Lab Partner	Locker/ Desk No.	Course & Section No.

Signature		Date	Witness/TA		Date

Exp. No.	Experiment/Subject		Date	
Name	Lab Partner		Locker/ Desk No.	Course & Section No.

Signature		Date	Witness/TA		Date

Exp. No.	Experiment/Subject		Date	
Name		Lab Partner	Locker/ Desk No.	Course & Section No.

Signature		Date	Witness/TA		Date

THE HAYDEN-McNEIL STUDENT LAB NOTEBOOK

Exp. No.	Experiment/Subject		Date		07
Name		Lab Partner	Locker/ Desk No.	Course & Section No.	

Signature		Date	Witness/TA		Date

Exp. No.	Experiment/Subject		Date	
Name	Lab Partner		Locker/ Desk No.	Course & Section No.

Signature		Date	Witness/TA		Date

Exp. No.	Experiment/Subject		Date	
Name	Lab Partner		Locker/ Desk No.	Course & Section No.

Signature		Date	Witness/TA		Date

THE HAYDEN-McNEIL STUDENT LAB NOTEBOOK   Note: Insert Divider Under Copy Sheet Before Writing

Exp. No.	Experiment/Subject		Date	
Name		Lab Partner	Locker/ Desk No.	Course & Section No.

Signature		Date	Witness/TA		Date

THE HAYDEN-McNEIL STUDENT LAB NOTEBOOK

Exp. No.	Experiment/Subject		Date	
Name	Lab Partner		Locker/ Desk No.	Course & Section No.

Signature		Date	Witness/TA		Date

Exp. No.	Experiment/Subject		Date	
Name	Lab Partner		Locker/Desk No.	Course & Section No.

Signature	Date	Witness/TA		Date

Note: Insert Divider Under Copy Sheet Before Writing

Exp. No.	Experiment/Subject		Date	
Name	Lab Partner		Locker/ Desk No.	Course & Section No.

Signature		Date	Witness/TA		Date

Exp. No.	Experiment/Subject		Date	
Name	Lab Partner		Locker/Desk No.	Course & Section No.

Signature		Date	Witness/TA		Date	

Exp. No.	Experiment/Subject		Date	11
Name		Lab Partner	Locker/ Desk No.	Course & Section No.

Signature		Date	Witness/TA		Date

Exp. No.	Experiment/Subject		Date	
Name	Lab Partner		Locker/ Desk No.	Course & Section No.

12

Signature	Date	Witness/TA	Date

THE HAYDEN-McNEIL STUDENT LAB NOTEBOOK

Note: Insert Divider Under Copy Sheet Before Writing

Exp. No.	Experiment/Subject		Date	
Name	Lab Partner		Locker/ Desk No.	Course & Section No.

12

COPY

Signature	Date	Witness/TA	Date

THE HAYDEN-McNEIL STUDENT LAB NOTEBOOK

Note: Insert Divider Under Copy Sheet Before Writing

Exp. No.	Experiment/Subject		Date	13
Name	Lab Partner		Locker/ Desk No.	Course & Section No.

Signature		Date	Witness/TA		Date

THE HAYDEN-McNEIL STUDENT LAB NOTEBOOK

Note: Insert Divider Under Copy Sheet Before Writing

Exp. No.	Experiment/Subject		Date	
Name	Lab Partner		Locker/ Desk No.	Course & Section No.

Signature		Date	Witness/TA		Date

Exp. No.	Experiment/Subject		Date	
Name	Lab Partner		Locker/ Desk No.	Course & Section No.

Signature		Date	Witness/TA		Date

Exp. No.	Experiment/Subject		Date	
Name	Lab Partner		Locker/ Desk No.	Course & Section No.

Signature		Date	Witness/TA		Date

Exp. No.	Experiment/Subject		Date	15
Name	Lab Partner		Locker/ Desk No.	Course & Section No.

Signature		Date	Witness/TA		Date

Exp. No.	Experiment/Subject		Date	
Name	Lab Partner		Locker/ Desk No.	Course & Section No.

15

COPY

Signature		Date	Witness/TA		Date

THE HAYDEN-McNEIL STUDENT LAB NOTEBOOK

Note: Insert Divider Under Copy Sheet Before Writing

Exp. No.	Experiment/Subject		Date	
Name	Lab Partner		Locker/ Desk No.	Course & Section No.

Signature	Date	Witness/TA		Date

THE HAYDEN-McNEIL STUDENT LAB NOTEBOOK

Note: Insert Divider Under Copy Sheet Before Writing

Exp. No.	Experiment/Subject		Date	
Name	Lab Partner		Locker/ Desk No.	Course & Section No.

Signature		Date	Witness/TA		Date

Note: Insert Divider Under Copy Sheet Before Writing

Exp. No.	Experiment/Subject		Date	
Name	Lab Partner		Locker/Desk No.	Course & Section No.

Signature		Date	Witness/TA		Date

Exp. No.	Experiment/Subject		Date	17
Name		Lab Partner	Locker/ Desk No.	Course & Section No.

Signature	Date	Witness/TA	Date

Note: Insert Divider Under Copy Sheet Before Writing

Exp. No.	Experiment/Subject		Date	
Name	Lab Partner		Locker/ Desk No.	Course & Section No.

Signature		Date	Witness/TA		Date

Exp. No.	Experiment/Subject		Date	
Name		Lab Partner	Locker/ Desk No.	Course & Section No.

Signature		Date	Witness/TA		Date

Exp. No.	Experiment/Subject		Date	
Name	Lab Partner		Locker/ Desk No.	Course & Section No.

Signature		Date	Witness/TA		Date

Exp. No.	Experiment/Subject		Date		19
Name		Lab Partner		Locker/Desk No.	Course & Section No.

Signature		Date	Witness/TA		Date

Note: Insert Divider Under Copy Sheet Before Writing

Exp. No.	Experiment/Subject		Date	
Name		Lab Partner	Locker/ Desk No.	Course & Section No.

Signature		Date	Witness/TA		Date

Exp. No.	Experiment/Subject		Date	
Name	Lab Partner		Locker/ Desk No.	Course & Section No.

Signature		Date	Witness/TA		Date

Exp. No.	Experiment/Subject		Date	
Name		Lab Partner	Locker/ Desk No.	Course & Section No.

Signature		Date	Witness/TA		Date

Exp. No.	Experiment/Subject		Date	
Name		Lab Partner	Locker/ Desk No.	Course & Section No.

Signature		Date	Witness/TA	Date

Exp. No.	Experiment/Subject		Date	
Name		Lab Partner	Locker/ Desk No.	Course & Section No.

22

Signature		Date	Witness/TA		Date

THE HAYDEN-McNEIL STUDENT LAB NOTEBOOK

Note: Insert Divider Under Copy Sheet Before Writing

Exp. No.	Experiment/Subject		Date	
Name	Lab Partner		Locker/ Desk No.	Course & Section No.

Signature		Date	Witness/TA	Date

Exp. No.	Experiment/Subject		Date	
Name		Lab Partner	Locker/ Desk No.	Course & Section No.

Signature		Date	Witness/TA		Date

Exp. No.	Experiment/Subject		Date	
Name	Lab Partner		Locker/ Desk No.	Course & Section No.

Signature		Date	Witness/TA		Date

Exp. No.	Experiment/Subject		Date	
Name	Lab Partner		Locker/ Desk No.	Course & Section No.

Signature		Date	Witness/TA		Date

Exp. No.	Experiment/Subject		Date	
Name	Lab Partner		Locker/ Desk No.	Course & Section No.

COPY

Signature		Date	Witness/TA	Date

Exp. No.	Experiment/Subject		Date	
Name		Lab Partner	Locker/ Desk No.	Course & Section No.

Signature		Date	Witness/TA		Date

Exp. No.	Experiment/Subject		Date	
Name		Lab Partner	Locker/ Desk No.	Course & Section No.

26

Exp. No.	Experiment/Subject		Date	
Name	Lab Partner		Locker/ Desk No.	Course & Section No.

Signature	Date	Witness/TA		Date

THE HAYDEN-McNEIL STUDENT LAB NOTEBOOK

Note: Insert Divider Under Copy Sheet Before Writing

Exp. No.	Experiment/Subject		Date	
Name		Lab Partner	Locker/ Desk No.	Course & Section No.

Signature		Date	Witness/TA		Date

Exp. No.	Experiment/Subject		Date	27
Name	Lab Partner		Locker/ Desk No.	Course & Section No.

Signature	Date	Witness/TA	Date

THE HAYDEN-McNEIL STUDENT LAB NOTEBOOK

Note: Insert Divider Under Copy Sheet Before Writing

Exp. No.	Experiment/Subject		Date	27
Name		Lab Partner	Locker/ Desk No.	Course & Section No.

COPY

Signature		Date	Witness/TA		Date

Exp. No.	Experiment/Subject		Date	
Name	Lab Partner		Locker/ Desk No.	Course & Section No.

Signature	Date	Witness/TA		Date

Note: Insert Divider Under Copy Sheet Before Writing

Exp. No.	Experiment/Subject		Date	
Name	Lab Partner		Locker/ Desk No.	Course & Section No.

Signature		Date	Witness/TA		Date

Exp. No.	Experiment/Subject		Date	
Name	Lab Partner		Locker/ Desk No.	Course & Section No.

Signature		Date	Witness/TA		Date

Exp. No.	Experiment/Subject		Date	29
Name	Lab Partner		Locker/ Desk No.	Course & Section No.

Signature	Date	Witness/TA	Date

Exp. No.	Experiment/Subject		Date	
Name		Lab Partner	Locker/ Desk No.	Course & Section No.

Signature		Date	Witness/TA		Date

Note: Insert Divider Under Copy Sheet Before Writing

Exp. No.	Experiment/Subject		Date	
Name	Lab Partner		Locker/ Desk No.	Course & Section No.

COPY

Signature	Date	Witness/TA		Date

Exp. No.	Experiment/Subject		Date	
Name		Lab Partner	Locker/ Desk No.	Course & Section No.

Signature		Date	Witness/TA		Date

THE HAYDEN-McNEIL STUDENT LAB NOTEBOOK

Note: Insert Divider Under Copy Sheet Before Writing

Exp. No.	Experiment/Subject		Date	31
Name	Lab Partner		Locker/ Desk No.	Course & Section No.

Signature	Date	Witness/TA	Date

Note: Insert Divider Under Copy Sheet Before Writing

Exp. No.	Experiment/Subject		Date	
Name	Lab Partner		Locker/ Desk No.	Course & Section No.

Signature		Date	Witness/TA		Date

Exp. No.	Experiment/Subject		Date	
Name	Lab Partner		Locker/ Desk No.	Course & Section No.

Signature		Date	Witness/TA		Date

Note: Insert Divider Under Copy Sheet Before Writing

Exp. No.	Experiment/Subject		Date	
Name		Lab Partner	Locker/ Desk No.	Course & Section No.

Signature	Date	Witness/TA	Date

Exp. No.	Experiment/Subject		Date	
Name	Lab Partner		Locker/ Desk No.	Course & Section No.

Signature	Date	Witness/TA	Date

Note: Insert Divider Under Copy Sheet Before Writing

34

Exp. No.	Experiment/Subject		Date	
Name		Lab Partner	Locker/ Desk No.	Course & Section No.

Signature		Date	Witness/TA		Date

THE HAYDEN-McNEIL STUDENT LAB NOTEBOOK

Note: Insert Divider Under Copy Sheet Before Writing

Exp. No.	Experiment/Subject		Date	
Name	Lab Partner		Locker/ Desk No.	Course & Section No.

Signature		Date	Witness/TA		Date

Note: Insert Divider Under Copy Sheet Before Writing

Exp. No.	Experiment/Subject		Date	
Name	Lab Partner		Locker/ Desk No.	Course & Section No.

Signature		Date	Witness/TA		Date

Exp. No.	Experiment/Subject		Date	
Name	Lab Partner		Locker/ Desk No.	Course & Section No.

Signature		Date	Witness/TA		Date

Note: Insert Divider Under Copy Sheet Before Writing

Exp. No.	Experiment/Subject		Date	
Name	Lab Partner		Locker/ Desk No.	Course & Section No.

Signature		Date	Witness/TA		Date

Exp. No.	Experiment/Subject		Date	
Name	Lab Partner		Locker/ Desk No.	Course & Section No.

36

Signature		Date	Witness/TA	Date

THE HAYDEN-McNEIL STUDENT LAB NOTEBOOK

Note: Insert Divider Under Copy Sheet Before Writing

Exp. No.	Experiment/Subject		Date	
Name	Lab Partner		Locker/ Desk No.	Course & Section No.

Signature		Date	Witness/TA		Date

Exp. No.	Experiment/Subject		Date	
Name	Lab Partner		Locker/ Desk No.	Course & Section No.

Signature		Date	Witness/TA		Date

Exp. No.	Experiment/Subject		Date	
Name	Lab Partner		Locker/ Desk No.	Course & Section No.

Signature		Date	Witness/TA		Date

Exp. No.	Experiment/Subject		Date	
Name	Lab Partner		Locker/ Desk No.	Course & Section No.

38

Signature	Date	Witness/TA	Date

THE HAYDEN-McNEIL STUDENT LAB NOTEBOOK　　Note: Insert Divider Under Copy Sheet Before Writing

Exp. No.	Experiment/Subject		Date	39
Name	Lab Partner		Locker/Desk No.	Course & Section No.

Signature	Date	Witness/TA		Date

THE HAYDEN-McNEIL STUDENT LAB NOTEBOOK

Note: Insert Divider Under Copy Sheet Before Writing

Exp. No.	Experiment/Subject		Date	39
Name	Lab Partner		Locker/ Desk No.	Course & Section No.

COPY

Signature	Date	Witness/TA		Date

THE HAYDEN-McNEIL STUDENT LAB NOTEBOOK

Note: Insert Divider Under Copy Sheet Before Writing

Exp. No.	Experiment/Subject		Date	
Name	Lab Partner		Locker/ Desk No.	Course & Section No.

Signature		Date	Witness/TA		Date

Note: Insert Divider Under Copy Sheet Before Writing

Exp. No.	Experiment/Subject		Date	
Name	Lab Partner		Locker/ Desk No.	Course & Section No.

Signature		Date	Witness/TA		Date

Exp. No.	Experiment/Subject		Date	
Name	Lab Partner		Locker/ Desk No.	Course & Section No.

Signature	Date	Witness/TA		Date

Exp. No.	Experiment/Subject		Date	
Name		Lab Partner	Locker/ Desk No.	Course & Section No.

Signature		Date	Witness/TA		Date	

Note: Insert Divider Under Copy Sheet Before Writing

Exp. No.	Experiment/Subject		Date	
Name		Lab Partner	Locker/ Desk No.	Course & Section No.

Exp. No.	Experiment/Subject		Date	
Name	Lab Partner		Locker/ Desk No.	Course & Section No.

Signature	Date	Witness/TA	Date

Exp. No.	Experiment/Subject		Date	
Name	Lab Partner		Locker/ Desk No.	Course & Section No.

Signature		Date	Witness/TA		Date

Exp. No.	Experiment/Subject		Date	
Name	Lab Partner		Locker/ Desk No.	Course & Section No.

Signature		Date	Witness/TA		Date

Exp. No.	Experiment/Subject		Date	
Name		Lab Partner	Locker/ Desk No.	Course & Section No.

Signature		Date	Witness/TA		Date

Note: Insert Divider Under Copy Sheet Before Writing

Exp. No.	Experiment/Subject		Date	
Name		Lab Partner	Locker/ Desk No.	Course & Section No.

Signature		Date	Witness/TA		Date

Exp. No.	Experiment/Subject		Date	
Name		Lab Partner	Locker/ Desk No.	Course & Section No.

Signature	Date	Witness/TA		Date

Exp. No.	Experiment/Subject		Date	45
Name	Lab Partner		Locker/ Desk No.	Course & Section No.

COPY

Signature	Date	Witness/TA	Date

THE HAYDEN-McNEIL STUDENT LAB NOTEBOOK Note: Insert Divider Under Copy Sheet Before Writing

Exp. No.	Experiment/Subject		Date	
Name		Lab Partner	Locker/ Desk No.	Course & Section No.

Signature		Date	Witness/TA		Date

Exp. No.	Experiment/Subject		Date	
Name	Lab Partner		Locker/ Desk No.	Course & Section No.

Signature		Date	Witness/TA		Date

Exp. No.	Experiment/Subject		Date	
Name		Lab Partner	Locker/ Desk No.	Course & Section No.

Signature		Date	Witness/TA	Date	

Note: Insert Divider Under Copy Sheet Before Writing

Exp. No.	Experiment/Subject		Date		47
Name	Lab Partner		Locker/ Desk No.	Course & Section No.	

Signature	Date	Witness/TA	Date

Exp. No.	Experiment/Subject		Date	
Name		Lab Partner	Locker/ Desk No.	Course & Section No.

Signature		Date	Witness/TA		Date

Exp. No.	Experiment/Subject		Date	
Name	Lab Partner		Locker/ Desk No.	Course & Section No.

COPY

Signature		Date	Witness/TA		Date

THE HAYDEN-McNEIL STUDENT LAB NOTEBOOK   Note: Insert Divider Under Copy Sheet Before Writing

Exp. No.	Experiment/Subject		Date	49
Name	Lab Partner		Locker/Desk No.	Course & Section No.

Signature		Date	Witness/TA		Date

THE HAYDEN-McNEIL STUDENT LAB NOTEBOOK   Note: Insert Divider Under Copy Sheet Before Writing

Exp. No.	Experiment/Subject		Date	
Name	Lab Partner		Locker/ Desk No.	Course & Section No.

Signature		Date	Witness/TA		Date

Exp. No.	Experiment/Subject		Date	
Name	Lab Partner		Locker/ Desk No.	Course & Section No.

Signature		Date	Witness/TA		Date

Note: Insert Divider Under Copy Sheet Before Writing

Exp. No.	Experiment/Subject		Date	
Name	Lab Partner		Locker/ Desk No.	Course & Section No.

Signature	Date	Witness/TA		Date

Note: Insert Divider Under Copy Sheet Before Writing